When You Feel Like Strangling The Patient

Love and Support For The Caregiver

Lauren Simon

Cover art and interior line drawings by Alexa Weisman.

alexaweisman93@gmail.com

Author photos courtesy of Rodelle Bas Portland, Oregon.

Firemen photo courtesy of Tualatin Valley Fire and Rescue.

Family photo courtesy of Stevi Sayler Photography.

Published by Waterfront Press

www.waterfrontdigitalpress.com

Cataloging-in Publication Data is on file with the Library of Congress.

ISBN: 1943625212

ISBN-13: 978-1943625215

For my Stephen

And

Our heroes

Lieutenant Paramedic Michael Thorne

Engineer Paramedic Shawn Suing

Firefighter Paramedic Michael Doty

Firefighter Paramedic Daniel Hastie

And Lastly

My son Carter who is now training to become a Firefighter Paramedic because of his personal experience that fateful evening in November.

CONTENTS

"There are four kinds of people in this world: those who have been caregivers, those who currently are caregivers, those who will be caregivers, and those who will need caregivers."

~ Rosalynn Carter

FOREWORD

"I'll take your part

When darkness comes

And pain is all around

Like a bridge over troubled waters

I will lay me down."

~Paul Simon "Bridge over Troubled Waters."

While considering how to write this foreword, I kept remembering a scene in the movie Reds in which Warren Beatty tries to convince Diane Keaton to travel with him to New York.

1

"What as?" Ms. Keaton asks.

"What do you mean?" Mr. Beatty responds.

"I mean what as? Your lover, your partner, your concubine, your friend, your wife, your protector? What as?"

To which Mr. Beatty responds, "Well, it's almost Thanksgiving. Why don't you come as a turkey?"

And that's me. The early Thanksgiving turkey who had the bad manners, bad timing, bad judgment and really bad listening skills to die four times on November 3, 2011 and in so doing scare the hell out of my wife, my family, my friends, and myself.

But mostly my wife, the woman who had transformed my life in more magical ways than I could ever begin to describe. The woman who had finally, after more than sixty years of life, cured me of my abandonment fears. Who had taught me what true, lasting love from a strong, wise woman looks like. Who had become the mother figure to my daughters after they had spent almost two decades with me as their single parent. Who had become my lover, my best friend, my biggest fan, my shelter, my solace, my inspiration, and my greatest joy.

And who had literally begged me for years to change my diet and exercise habits so that I wouldn't have a heart attack and die. Everything, and I mean everything, that you will read in this book is true. Some of it has even been muted and downplayed by Lauren so as not to embarrass me. For instance, she mentions that I apologized to her for months after my heart attack. I sure did, and have kept on doing so on a regular basis. I plan to keep on apologizing to her for the rest of my life.

If there was any one thing in my life for which I would appreciate a do-over, it would be wiping out that awful experience. Not for me. I was drugged and pampered through most of the toughest parts of the whole thing and have become a different (and I hope wiser) person in many ways as a result. No, not for me...but for my family and friends, and mostly for Lauren who deserved, and will always deserve, much better.

As Lauren writes, even the darkest hours of our lives contain gifts for our evolution as human beings. My heart attack was no exception. The inspiration for this book came to Lauren out of that experience. I am beyond grateful that it did because I can now hope that others will benefit from reading about what I did, and didn't do, and then protect themselves and their own loved ones from going through what we did.

Hopefully too, those of you who are caregivers will also now feel more freedom to express your own needs and wants. When Lauren found that many other caregivers experienced the same feelings of anger, resentment, and loneliness that she encountered but didn't feel that it was "right" or "their place" to even mention those feelings, let alone demand that they be respected and acknowledged, she knew that she had to write this book.

Being as honest as Lauren is in these pages is an act of incredible vulnerability. Even though she knows that some might find her honesty a bit shocking, she is committed to letting other caregivers know that they are not alone and have every right to stand up for themselves, even as they care for their loved ones.

One of my hopes for this book too is that it will help give others a better understanding of how to ease the burdens on the caregivers who shoulder the majority of the responsibility but too often receive a minimum amount of understanding and appreciation. As one who was the patient, I know firsthand how tough your challenges are as a caregiver. Bless you for your love, compassion, and patience.

My wife is one brave woman. And I am one very lucky guy to have had Lauren build a bridge over troubled waters and help me to the other side.

Lastly, I have a message for my male brethren:

Intuition is not a myth. If your partner loves you and shares a deeply felt intuition with you, pay close attention. I didn't, and died four times. I somehow came back. But don't trust that you will be as lucky as I was.

And remember that our partner's willingness to help us heal our wounds, physical and emotional, and their courage to tell us the truth, even when it may be painful or embarrassing, are acts of pure love for which we should be eternally grateful during every single moment of this delightful and amazing experience that we call life.

Stephen Simon

West Linn, Oregon

CHAPTER ONE

Welcome To The Gang

"We are more alike, my friends, than we are unalike." ~ Maya Angelou

Don't you just hate it when you have a feeling so horrible that it makes you cringe? Like having an urge to yell at (or, worse yet, strangle) the person you love the most—even as they lay sick in bed, needing continual care?

Wait a minute. I'm going too fast. So let me back up.

In the middle of an otherwise ordinary autumn night, I opened the bathroom door just in time to see my husband stumble out of the shower and drop to the floor, clutching his chest. I knew he was having a heart attack. What I didn't know is that he was about to die.

And be brought back to life.

Then clinically die again.

And be brought back once more.

And then have his heart stop two more times before that horrible night was finally over.

Nor did I understand what living through this experience would do to me. Or what I was in for during the weeks, and months that lay ahead.

If I had an inkling of what to expect, even just a tiny understanding of what the immediate change in our lives would look like, would it have lessened that drama and reduced my own stress level—to say nothing of my husband's—in the days that followed?

Uh, yes. Would the same be true for you? Probably

yes.

Because I was totally unprepared for what happened in the aftermath of becoming a Sudden Caregiver does not mean that you have to be. This role is far too important to step into without any idea of what could be ahead and how to deal with it. So I'm glad you picked up this book. I wish anyone would be given a book similar to this one in coping with a horrible experience like that which my family and I went through.

It may at times seem as though this book is about me, as I intermittently share my personal story with you. Make no mistake though. This book is about you. What I want to impress upon you by sharing my journey—and specifically the following passage—is that very often we become caregivers suddenly, and without warning.

The Night My Husband Died

Stephen was screaming, his voice filled with terror, and I was trying to think straight. He was calling out in an end-of-life panic as I ran out of the bathroom. While I was racing for the phone to dial 9-1-1, all my husband knew was that I suddenly wasn't there and that he was lying all alone on a stone cold floor, a searing pain in his chest taking his breath away—literally.

I fumbled, temporarily forgetting how to use our home phone. Then eventually found myself talking with a 9-1-1 operator while Stephen was still screaming in terror.

She assertively, but gently, told me to calm my husband and comfort him as best I could, assuring him that help was just minutes away. The operator offered to stay on the line, but I hung up instinctively and ran back to kneel down next to Stephen.

He looked at me wild-eyed. I said, "Honey, help is on the way, minutes away. Just focus on breathing." He calmed the tiniest bit. "Good," I praised. "Just keep your focus on breathing. They'll be here in a second."

I continued reassuring my husband over and over with positive messages to help calm him all the while silently praying he would make it until assistance arrived. I was also cleaning him up and attempting to get some fresh underwear on him in order to protect his modesty. I rapidly scooped up anything with expelled body fluids on them (his sandals, bathrobe, towels, rugs), running out for a second to toss them into the washer in the laundry room down the hall. Then was back before I hoped he even knew I had left.

"Honey, help is on the way, help is on the way." I repeated. "Just focus on breathing. Good. Just keep your focus on breathing. They'll be here in a second."

When I felt I had calmed him just a little, I said, "I'll be right back, right back," kissed his forehead, then ran upstairs to wake up my then fifteen-year-old son (Stephen's stepson), Carter. I gently shook him. "Honey, you need to wake up. Stephen is having a heart attack and I need your help. I need you to watch out front and yell for me when the paramedics arrive." I also needed his help on another front: settling Lola—our five-year-old stocky yellow lab had sensed the trauma and was barking ferociously.

Downstairs again, I moved about the house to prepare for the paramedics to arrive. By then, Stephen's screams had turned to moans. Strangely, the sound comforted me. It meant he was alive. I urgently wanted the first responders to arrive.

I had never seen my husband with so much panic in his eyes. I tried hard. I tried so very hard to keep the alarm out of my own voice and behavior. I don't think I did, but I tried. I didn't know if my dearest, most beloved person in the world would last until someone got there. It looked as if he might not. It felt as if he wouldn't. But thank God, he did.

However, this book isn't about that miraculous rescue... it's about the weeks and months later, when I was wondering whether I would make it until help for me arrived.

Oh, help arrived pretty quickly in the form of love and homemade cooked meals. Yes, such beautiful help and supportive assistance arrived literally overnight. But help with what I was going through as a newly anointed caregiver, or help with the aggressive emotions that were popping up inside of me, did not come.

What I desperately needed was information about what to expect when anger and exhaustion arises from caregiving. Or even just the basics of what might be encountered. Sort of a "What To Expect When You're Caregiving" guide.

I needed to know all of the ins and outs of how to best care for someone I loved during the critical months of a medical crisis—and how to best care for myself while I was doing it. The gap in my understanding about what to do next and what to avoid, was big. Actually, it was huge.

I needed data. I'd been thrown into a data gap and what I needed to know could fill a book. And it has. Well, really, you're holding it.

I wish I had this book in my hands when I left the hospital still trembling from the experience, while carrying piles of information on how to best care for Stephen however nothing on how to care for myself or for my family in crisis. I wish someone had given me a book like this before the horrible fleeting thought that I wanted to strangle my husband crossed my mind (Chapter Eight, Woman Gone Wild). But, of course, it didn't exist. I had to write it. So I did with the intent that you have the information when you need it most.

My prayer is that hospitals and physician's offices begin handing it out at the same time they hand out Care of the Patient literature—so that no one is ever in the position that millions of other Sudden Caregivers have been in.

Welcome. It is good that you have come here. To a place where you'll find help in doing well and being well, even as someone you love is seeking to get well. No matter that their prospects of getting well may be slim, or that they may be living the final moments of their life, there is a way for both of you to travel well on that journey.

Shall we unfold the map?

CHAPTER TWO

Shaken Awake

"Bravery is being the only one who knows you're afraid."

~Franklin P. Jones

Let's start by exploring what a caregiving journey could look like, which we'll do as I continue to share my personal story with you. Then, we'll look at other related stories that might mirror your own, assuming you're already in, have been in, or will be in a caregiving situation.

Most importantly, we will consider solutions throughout this book that will not only aid you in moving through your caregiving journey, but also assist you in using your experience to make choices that can shape the rest of your life. For example, consider the possibility that your caregiving journey can aid you in designing a life that you may have only imagined. When we put ourselves aside to care for someone else, our own needs (perhaps ones we have long been ignoring) become clear. These needs, these desires, and even fears, become painfully obvious as they begin to shout out and demand that we take notice.

So your caregiving journey can be a treasure map, showing you the way to declaring your needs and desires. But first, your only goal is to be as present and as aware in your current situation as you possibly can be.

The night my husband died four times was very dreamlike. I even questioned whether it was really happening. At times, I felt as if I was out of my own body, hovering above somewhere, watching the entire scene unfold beneath me—I was a part of the picture, and yet I was far away.

It was surreal to see the quiet, flashing lights on top of the red fire truck in the middle of a foggy night as the first firefighter/paramedic walked up our steps, emerging as if from a cloud, lugging bulky equipment. The visual actually reminded me of a scene from the film, E.T. The Extra Terrestrial.

As the first fireman stepped into our home, I began to tell him where Stephen was, but he cut me off. "Secure the dog," he ordered, as Lola barked even more ferociously than before. Carter was right there to take over with Lola, who is ordinarily a kind, gentle dog, but was obviously panicked. And she did not go with him willingly. Carter, who is a strong "weight lifting" young man, struggled with all of his strength to pull Lola up the stairs and shut her in the master bedroom.

The minute one of the firemen reached my husband, Stephen slumped over unconscious and slid sideways down the wall where he was propped. His lifeless body was dragged and laid flat in front of his large screen television on the cold tile floor.

His underwear was immediately cut off him. So much for my modesty plan. CPR was initiated and a fireman began asking me questions while steering me away from Stephen so the team could do its work.

Distracted by the severity of the situation and the sight of my unconscious, colorless husband on the floor, I couldn't remember his age or his birthday, even though I was holding his driver's license and insurance cards so tightly that they made imprints in my palm. The fireman who was asking me questions noticed my disorientation and gently took the license and card from my hand, writing down all the information he needed.

At that point, Stephen's breathing became loud and labored...unlike anything I had ever heard. His body was desperately trying to gasp for breath. The paramedics were in the process of hooking him up to a defibrillator and inserting needles in his arm when his breathing completely stopped.

The reality was this journey we were being taken on...was taking us straight into the heartbeat of our lives and frankly, was more terrifying than anything I'd ever known.

LAUREN SIMON

CHAPTER THREE

You Call This A Journey?

"This is 'reality', Greg."

~Elliot in the film E.T.: The Extraterrestrial

As I hovered over my unconscious husband, one of the three fireman surrounding him yelled, "Stephen, this is going to hurt!" before shocking his heart with a defibrillator in order to get it pumping regularly again. (Stephen's ribs were indeed sore for almost two months after. We were both later told that ribs are often broken in those kinds of life-threatening moments.)

The fireman who had taken Stephen's license and medical cards then tried to lead me upstairs to the main level, but I hesitated and saw Stephen's body jolt off the floor as soon as the defibrillator shocked his heart for the second time. That one image—my husband's naked, lifeless, colorless body bouncing off the tile floor—is not one that I will ever forget.

The firemen continued to talk loudly to Stephen and then...thank God...I heard him answer. "I can hear you. I can hear you. I am right here. Why are you yelling?"

He was back.

I was worried about Carter, so I listened to the fireman temporarily and went upstairs to find my son pacing in the kitchen. "He's going to be okay, sweetheart," I reassured him—while thinking to myself how desperately I wanted to believe what I was saying.

Stephen and Carter have a strong, impenetrable bond. Even though their "guy banter" sometimes makes me shake my head, I know they understand and adore each other. Stephen brings great comfort and a sense of safety to Carter's life. Carter brings joy, respect, and humor to Stephen's.

While I was comforting my son, trying to ease him out of the daze he was in, Stephen stopped responding again. I could "hear" his silence from the floor beneath us until the firemen once again loudly started talking to him.

I felt a chill—and Stephen's absence in the house. I felt his spirit had gone. Left. Disappeared. I waffled between an excruciating, intense sense of terror and a numbness devoid of any feeling. I started muttering, then began rocking myself to try to soothe my agony. I looked into my son's eyes, while asking myself out loud, "Is he really doing this? Is this really happening?" My words shifted to my own private thoughts: This is it. He really is leaving me and our family.

Carter held my face with both of his hands and said in a stern voice, "Look at me! Hold me tight. Don't let go." He hugged me tighter and longer than he had ever done as a young adult. After some time, I squeezed him reassuringly and thanked him before letting go. I felt a cloud of energy surround me. I prayed, begged, and pleaded inside my own heart and head, all on what felt like huge waves of emotion. Then, I demanded that my husband not go. I yelled inside my head, "No, Stephen, no! You are not going to leave us! No!" I don't know who I was commanding. Maybe I thought I was speaking to his soul.

Carter and I again heard the awful noises of the defibrillation process downstairs. The fireman called, "Clear!" followed by the frightening sound of the machine itself. And next the terrible, sickening thump of Stephen's body as the shock lifted him and then dropped him like a dead weight to the tile floor.

Again, the fireman: "Stephen! Stephen! Can you hear me?"

Silence.

More Silence.

A few more firemen chimed in, "Stephen! Stephen!

Can you hear us?"

Then in his normal everyday voice...."Yeah, of course I can hear you. Why are you all yelling at me?" Carter and I looked at each other and laughed out of pure relief.

We still chuckle about Stephen's matter-of-fact (and completely unaware) manner at that moment, but Carter would later say that hearing his step-dad respond was one of the happiest moments in his life.

It seemed as if hours had passed when in reality, all this had taken place in moments. The firemen asked us to go look for the ambulance, which had not yet arrived. I took that opportunity to quickly move our cars out of the garage so the arriving medical team could have easier access to the lower level of our house. I had hardly finished this when the ambulance pulled in.

Both Carter and I watched as the firemen and the ambulance crew strapped my naked husband, wrapped in a blanket, onto a gurney then carried him out through the garage. As I followed them out, Carter shouted, "Tell him I love him."

25

I stepped into the ambulance as far as I could and rested my hand on Stephen's leg saying, "I love you and Carter wants you to know he loves you, too."

One of the fireman, whom I would later found out was Lieutenant/Paramedic Mike Thorne, confirmed that I could go in the ambulance with Stephen, but added that he thought it might be best if I drove my own car. He cautioned me to take my time and not to rush to the hospital, as it was indeed a dark, foggy, night. He made sure that we were okay before he left, mentioning again that we had plenty of time, urging me to drive safely.

Plenty of time? It didn't feel like we had plenty of time.

And I was right.

Stephen died again on the way to the hospital.

CHAPTER FOUR

Don't Worry. Be Happy.

"I am beginning to learn that it is the sweet,
simple things of life

which are the real ones after all."

~Laura Ingalls Wilder

Just as our beloved pets can sense a dangerous
situation miles away, the human body can pick up
trauma before one consciously registers that it's
near. When the crisis gets more intense, the
internal message gets louder. That was certainly
the case for me as my body began to shake and I
uncontrollably started taking in deep breaths.

Carter was racing to grab a sweatshirt and some shoes so we could leave, while I quickly called my stepdaughter Heather and her fiancé (now husband) Eli, who lived together at the time in Northwest Portland, asking them to head to the hospital to meet us. "I don't want you to worry," I began my conversation with Heather. "Everything is fine now, but your dad has had a heart attack."

Even though I told her everything was fine, I didn't believe it. I wanted to believe it, but I was lying through my chattering teeth.

As we drove to the emergency room, I thanked Carter for his bravery in helping me. I reassured him that Stephen would pull through. What I didn't know in that moment was that Stephen's heart had stopped again in the ambulance. He had "died" but was brought back to life once again.

I could already see that the experience we'd just been through had scarred Carter deeply. And indeed, in the days, weeks, and months to come, he would need a lot of reassuring as he continually asked, "That's never going to happen again, is it?"

Carter and I bolted into Meridian Park Hospital. I

handled the admission information before a nurse led me by the Emergency Room waiting area. Heather was already there, slumped up against her Eli. Even though my urge was to get to my husband, I stopped quickly to hug them.

Heather, then 25, looked like a little girl to me in that moment. All I noticed were her freckles—and then a picture that I had seen of her dressed in a pumpkin costume when she was a child popped into my mind. I heard the song in my head that she used to sing: "Don't Worry. Be Happy".

Though this all took only a matter of seconds, something happens with time when danger blows in. It slows down, it bends, and it even stops if it is called to—experiencing this distortion in time can be a dreamlike feeling, in which time seems to fold in on itself and then expand. A logical explanation for such a shift does not exist. Perhaps it is not time at all that has changed, but our perception of it. Maybe in situations such as these, the human mind has the ability to slow down, to look into each moment more closely, nanosecond by nanosecond, and to notice much more of what is passing before us.

I remember experiencing this perception shift as a child when a tree sliced through our roof directly above me as I stood in front of the television watching Romper Room. I heard a loud voice ordering me to "RUN!" as I looked up and saw a ceiling light breaking into pieces seemingly in slow motion. A snow-topped tree speared through our roof while pieces of glass appeared to float through the air. But not a piece of glass touched me. There was no sound other than that urgent instruction to get out. The tree hit its bull's-eye right where I had been standing, with glass covering the entire living room floor, while I was safe outside, heart beating rapidly.

Walking quickly toward my husband in the hospital on that fateful, foggy evening, I prayed time would once again bend in my favor. When I arrived at the Emergency Room, there were five nurses surrounding my husband, who lay still with his eyes closed. I later learned that a specially trained heart attack team had been called by the firemen so that they were ready and waiting for Stephen's arrival.

A tall, handsome, silver-haired man, who would

come to be Stephen's new cardiologist, introduced himself as Dr. Miguel Gomez. He informed me that Stephen's heart had stopped again in the ambulance, that he had been "brought back to life." The doctor informed me that my husband had two blocked arteries, and that he would need to be immediately rushed into surgery so stents could be Inserted to open those blockages.

I moved over to Stephen's side, held his hand and spoke his name. "Open your eyes and look at me," I softly said. "I love you. Come back to me. This family needs you." Stephen opened his eyes and looked into mine. Then he nodded, as if to promise me that everything would be okay.

Dr. Gomez mentioned twice that Stephen was a very lucky man. The surgeon's confidence assured me and gave me comfort. What I didn't know then was that Stephen's heart would stop for a fourth time on the way into surgery. In total, his heart had stopped twice at home, once in the ambulance, and then again heading into the operation. This was a man who was fighting to live. A man with a strong heart.

I rejoined my family and we were brought to a private waiting room. Private waiting rooms are sometimes called "bad news" rooms, a place to keep the hysterical reactions and tears from others in "normal" waiting rooms. The personal attention that came with the room was comforting. A kind nurse gave me her phone number in case I needed her. She offered us all water and brought coffee for Heather.

There was a lot of back rubbing, checking in with each other, staring off into space, and talking about when to call the other siblings. Heather's sister, Cari, and my then nineteen-year-old daughter Brenna, both lived in Los Angeles at the time, while Stephen's other daughter Tabitha lived in San Antonio. With Brenna having a full day of school and Tabitha having a full day of work, I decided that it would be best to wait until morning to call them.

But Cari was self-employed and had a more flexible schedule. Even if she hadn't, I knew she would never have forgiven me if I didn't call and wake her then. She answered her phone on the first ring, "Hello, Nonna? What's wrong?"

"Honey, everything is fine now, but your father has had a heart attack and he is in surgery."

"Oh, my God. Is he going to be ok?" she asked, crying.

I assured her that he would be fine and that I would call back as soon as he was out of the operating room. With that, I handed the phone to Heather so Cari could make plans to fly in.

I walked the halls alone in shock. At last tears came. Then my body began to tremble again. I called the nurse and asked her to please check in on Stephen. A thoughtful janitor who saw me walking the halls and softly weeping, brought me Kleenex and asked if there was anything he could do. His tone made it clear he sincerely wanted to know. He cared.

I shook my head "no" and whispered, "Thanks." Then the nurse arrived, reporting that surgery was going as planned. Her knowing eyes brought me some peace. In that instant I was gently and lovingly being reminded that it is the sweet, simple gestures in life that mean the most to the heart and soul.

After what felt like an eternity, during which Time itself seemed to be pulled like taffy—then frozen in mid-pull—Dr. Gomez returned. "It went well," he said quietly. "A complete success." I almost melted. He found my hand and patted it for a moment. "You can see him in about half an hour," he said, answering the question I hadn't yet asked, but one he knew I was just about to. "He's in ICU."

Dr. Gomez mentioned again how fortunate Stephen was to get into surgery so quickly. "There's a mantra in emergency medicine and cardiology that time is muscle," he said. "What that means is, the longer the time that there's a lack of coronary blood flow, the more damage there is to the heart." Stephen was blessed with no damage to his heart. Thank God, time and heaven were both on our side.

Carter, Heather, Eli and I were all ushered into the ICU. Stephen opened his eyes, looked at me and just said, "Hey." After he said hello to Carter, Eli and Heather, he asked me, "It wasn't really that bad, was it? I didn't really have a heart attack, did I?" My first thought in response was what a miraculous thing the mind does to protect the soul it is accompanying.

Eventually, things slowly sank in and Stephen apologized to Carter for having to witness and experience what he did—and over the course of the next few weeks and months, he wouldn't stop apologizing to me. I believe Stephen processed nuggets of insight as he could handle them. We who are the loved ones of those in medical emergencies, however, face our own struggles with processing events. We can feel reluctant to open up, in part, because we want to protect the patient. This can lead to meltdowns, breakdowns, and if we are lucky, possibly even to breakthroughs.

CHAPTER FIVE

What About The Family?

"Call it a clan, call it a network, call it a tribe, call it a family. Whatever you call it, whoever you are, you need one". ~Jane Howard

While life and the medical community can be incredibly kind and protective of patients, the caregivers and loved ones also often face their own struggles. Fortunately, this is slowly changing.

I can only imagine what Cari and Brenna experienced so far away in L.A., each alone, during the early morning hours when they heard about Stephen's heart attack. Well, actually, I imagine they probably felt helpless not being able to do anything in the moment. I can also envision Tabitha experiencing one of her greatest fears about her father when I called her before dawn as well. Thankfully, she had her fiancé Felix holding her hand and urging her to get a ticket and go home to her Dad.

Brenna, Tabitha, Cari, Heather, and Eli did indeed come home. It was comforting to have everyone in the house and to feel their presence and love. They wouldn't have had it any other way. And even though I was struggling with the reality of what had happened, my goal was to remain strong in front of my family.

There wasn't much time for sleep, peace, rest, quiet or processing. I had relatives and friends to inform and talk to, laundry to do, phone calls and emails to respond to, and a home to prepare for the return of my husband, "the patient." I was beyond grateful and relieved that my life mate was alive. I wanted to see him, be with him, all of the time. I did not want him to feel that he was going through any of this alone. I knew that this was the greatest gift I could give him—this "not aloneness." It's the gift I would want, above all else.

So each morning I could barely wait until visiting hours began. And the moments it took for some of our girls to get dressed for the hospital seemed like an eternity. Actually, everything then felt big, intense, and not as it should be. For example, there was the twenty-minute wait in a crowded Starbucks parking lot because our grown children had to have their coffee. My insides were screaming with anxiety, "I JUST WANT TO GET TO THE HOSPITAL, PEOPLE!"

One morning, Heather even asked me if I wanted to stop for a nice breakfast on the way.

"Excuse me? Uh, that would be no."

I knew I was edgy when Brenna told me to "chill" after I had yelled upstairs for both she and

Heather to "get a move on it!"

In retrospect, and in fairness to us all, one doesn't always think or respond in a normal fashion after having just witnessed a traumatic or stressful event. I certainly didn't. I wanted our adult children to have their own needs met—such as getting their Starbuck's in the morning—but I also wanted to honor my husband's needs, one of which was getting to his side as soon as possible. An easy solution for a normal-thinking person would have been we all drive to the hospital together and then whoever desired a latte could take the car and go. Ah-ha! Genius! But who was thinking clearly? Not me.

What I hope you will remember is not to beat yourself up if you react as I did, with sharp responses that you later regret. "Not always reacting normally " is very normal. You are human, and you are going through an intense experience. So be gentle with yourself.

I would like to say that my family is truly wonderful. I adore every one of them, and their presence at a critical time brought me enormous comfort. But this book is not about that. This book is about the "other" feelings, the unexpected feelings, that arise while caregiving. Feelings that aren't easy or comfortable to experience, let alone talk about.

I have mentioned that a tragedy like this can jolt us into seeing things more clearly than before. In my case, I noticed how all of our children had grown up "miraculously," and that they are, and have always been, giving, generous, loving, thoughtful humans with whom I am proud to even be in the same room with.

All of our children, each in their own unique and loving way, did things to ease my burdens and show me just how much they love and appreciate this family and each other. Having them around the fire late at night after being at the hospital all day was better than any medicine a doctor could prescribe—but that doesn't mean there were not some tense moments. And that is an important part of this story, because I am trying to point out here that even with all of that love and support, I became filled with anxiety and, as much as I hate to admit it, fear.

Here we had just witnessed a beautiful miracle of my husband living through a massive cardiac arrest and his four near-death experiences, but I felt as if another heart attack might happen again at any moment. I was terrified. And temporarily lost faith and trust, even though I had every reason to embrace both more strongly and more presently than ever before.

My husband's heart attack was like an earthquake that left us all in some wreckage. Together, as a family, we had some rubble to walk through as we moved into a new way of being in the world. We had been shaken, and anything that wasn't real had fallen away, leaving us raw and exposed.

While after any medical trauma, a healing plan is set in place for the patient's recovery, no such plan is created for the recovery of the patient's loved ones. The family is largely on its own to deal with whatever fallout it has experienced, including traumatic feelings that may have been suppressed during the patient's sudden illness or health scare. This is complicated by some family members who may feel it inappropriate to talk about the challenges they're facing because of what the patient has gone through—and is still going through. For instance, my adult children didn't want to share how difficult this situation was on them because they didn't want to "burden the patient."

Eventually, after a few months had passed and they had returned to their normal lives, all of our children shared with me their own struggles, and the emotions that they were still dealing with because of their father's/stepfather's heart attack.

Early on, even before our children returned to their lives, we were surrounded with much love and support to help us through. It touched me dearly when friends, neighbors, and loved ones reached out to the entire family. I was moved by the abundance of meals that were delivered, not just because of the thoughtfulness of a home-cooked dinner, but because everybody in the house was being thought of and cared for.

Also, reading the many prayers and get well wishes for Stephen and our family on Facebook and Twitter moved me deeply. Actually, they touched all of us. Friends created prayer circles, provided flowers and fruit baskets, and even offered to walk our dog Lola. Those gestures showed that other people clearly understood it is not just the patient who needs prayers, love, care, and concern—even if the patient's family didn't consider those needs for itself.

Yet, in truth, at times some well-meaning support felt overwhelming. Such as when a newly divorced neighbor came by at inappropriate times, called when he was inebriated, emailed daily, and felt it was important to let me know whenever he was crying and how hard this had all been on him. I knew he meant well, and that he was going through his own struggles, but these interactions were incredibly draining at the time.

When I shared this confusing behavior with other friends, I was surprised to learn that they had similar "caregiving" stories of when well-meaning support had turned overwhelming or draining. "It is almost as if people are in shock and want to act quickly to help, but instead, they step over some very common boundaries such as calling at inappropriate times, one friend added.

I have to admit that many months later, when a dear friend's daughter was badly injured in a horse accident, I was deeply upset. Even though I knew better, I reached out to the beyond-overwhelmed mother. I needed to let her know how much I loved the family and that my tears and prayers were flowing. I even contacted her other daughter, whom I love and adore and helped care for when she was young, to let her know how loved they all were. After I had done all of this, I realized that I possibly had been draining, though well-intentioned.

Another former caregiver agreed completely and jumped in to share his experience. "I know! A co-worker of mine found out that my wife was in the hospital and immediately called around midnight and woke me up while I was desperately trying to get caught up on lost sleep. I wondered if he had temporarily lost his mind."

This kind of thing continued happening for us beyond just the troublesome neighbor. The doorbell rang, the phone rang, various family member's cell phones rang, emails and texts poured in. As my head, reactions, and life were literally spinning with so many friends wanting to reach out and help, my sister-in-law Susan Granger and her husband James Mapes, gave me great comfort—and strict guidelines to follow.

James had undergone open-heart surgery the year before, so Susan knew all too well about the overwhelm that a caregiver experiences. The guidelines that she and James pointed out helped ease the burdens I felt, and actually helped nurture me back. Please see Appendix A: A Caregivers Survival Guide to Sanity. For Caregivers Guide & Checklist for Helpers, see Appendix B.

I do think it is important to spread some awareness, or a gentle reminder, on how overwhelmed the family of the patient could be and how important and respectful it is to tread lightly. At times, the family may not know how to handle all of the energy pouring in, coupled with the extra fatigue, overwhelming emotions, extreme stress and anxiety they're likely experiencing. So pray powerfully behind the scenes. But proceed slowly because the caregiver and each family member could possibly be on the verge of snapping, cracking, and popping.

CHAPTER SIX

Post Traumatic Stress Disorder

"Too often we underestimate the power of a touch, a smile, a kind word, a listening ear, an honest compliment, or the smallest act of caring, all of which have the potential to turn a life around." ~ Leo Buscaglia

It is important to understand that the reasons why caregivers and loved ones may feel overwhelmed by well-meaning support is that they may still be in shock, and possibly could be suffering from post traumatic stress disorder (PTSD).

The National Center for PTSD describes the disorder this way: "Posttraumatic Stress Disorder (PTSD) is an anxiety disorder that can occur following the experience or witnessing of a traumatic event."

Anyone who has been a victim of, or has witnessed or has been exposed to a life-threatening situation, or trauma, can develop PTSD. For instance, witnessing a heart attack, stroke or other potentially fatal situation involving a loved one will most likely make you a candidate for PTSD. Or, being informed of, or worse, witnessing your child experiencing a serious accident or contracting a devastating illness makes you susceptible to PTSD as well.

A Special Mention: Those Who Keep Us Safe

Veterans of war are prone to suffer from PTSD as are active duty members of the military in battle zones. Firefighters, police, emergency medical first responders, whose lives constantly encompass life-threatening danger, are also at constant risk for PTSD. In addition, these men and women in uniform have "hero identities" placed on them, along with the expectation to not get harmed, affected, injured, and even to not feel anxiety. This, in turn, magnifies the stress and the possibility of PTSD in their lives.

We civilians understand that these first responders must be exposed to dangerous situations in order to accomplish their mission of keeping us alive and safe. I have to think that at times they must feel alone and likely experience the world much differently than the rest of us do. They, in essence, have given a great part of their lives so that we may live ours. The amount of stress and pressure they have accepted in order to fulfill their life mission is something most of us cannot even imagine living with on a regular basis.

First responder teams have quite a unique bond. Often, they have nowhere to turn but to each other, possibly not even wanting to reach out to a life partner who could possibly understand, but whom they do not wish to burden.

Reaching out for psychological help may not be as easy for them as it is for us, as it clashes with those hero expectations and other pressures to "just deal with it." For them, getting help also can carry the stigma of not being able to handle the job and could be viewed as being detrimental to their career stability and advancement. Hopefully now, with so much tragedy and devastation after 9/11, the Boston Marathon bombings, school shootings, and the South Carolina church massacre, and sadly many other tragedies, our subsequent experience of these tragic events continue to open our hearts, and our deepening societal understanding of PTSD.

I have personally been thinking about the firefighters who saved my husband's life, and I will do so for the rest of my life. They shared with us that they often don't experience the success of someone like Stephen living through what he did. The self-doubt that might arise for them after not being able to help someone survive might even feel devastating, leaving them to possibly question themselves for the rest of their lives, although there should be no self-blame at all.

If you are firefighter or law enforcement officer, emergency medical first responder, military member, or war veteran, please know that the people of the world—people all around you—have so much gratitude for what you do. And know also, most importantly, that we want you safe and as healthy—mentally, physically and emotionally—as possible. Thank you for your service in our world, and may God bless your hearts and those you love.

For The Rest Of Us

Very often in life we too can experience more than one event that triggers PTSD. While it is important to understand that PTSD can be treated, the vivid memories of the traumatic event itself may never go away. Even so, there are many ways to soften the memories and manage healthier responses to those triggers. There are many ways to seek peace and wholeness and we will touch on those shortly. First though, let's look at what PTSD might look like for a caregiver.

What Happens?

When something triggers a past traumatic experience, patients, caregivers, and family members who suffer from PTSD might feel as if the event is happening all over again. For instance, friends of mine who were notified by telephone of their son's terrible car accident became incredibly alarmed every time the phone rang. Just the sound of the ringing set off the same panic through their bodies and minds that they experienced when they received the initial call about their son.

My stepdaughter Heather mentioned that for a while after her father's heart attack, my phone calls triggered alarm for her too. Even if she was busy, she couldn't proceed with what she had to do until she called me back or listened to my message to find out if everything was okay with her father. The same proved true for my daughter Brenna. My call to her about Stephen was made early in the morning. If I am aware she is headed to a job early and I call her on the way, she still answers worriedly asking, if everything is all right before saying "hello," even though it has now been over a year since his heart attack.

The mind of the person experiencing PTSD might know the event is not actually recurring, yet the body responds as if it is. Emotions may feel over the top. Impatience and anger may surface. Layer embarrassment and confusion with those intense emotions and you've got some "stuff" to deal with for sure.

Symptoms of PTSD may look or feel like depression, panic, and/or anxiety attacks. In addition, those suffering from PTSD may constantly be on the alert or on guard, causing normal reactions to escalate beyond what is ordinary. These reactions can create problems in trying to live a healthy life. If not treated appropriately, withdrawal or isolation may occur. Also, substance abuse or other addictions may develop in order to numb feelings that then can give an illusion of being safe in a life that actually is out of control.

One caregiving confidant, who eventually left her husband after he continuously threatened suicide with a gun in his hand, told me that once when she heard the ordinary sound of an ice machine dispensing in her refrigerator, "I hit the floor, thinking it was gun shots. My heart was pounding and I was terrified." It took some time before she realized, after lying on her kitchen floor unable to move, that it was a normal everyday sound that had became something very different and dangerous in her mind, and therefore in her life.

She went on to explain years later, then happily remarried, that her PTSD never completely subsided. "My husband and I were renovating. He was carrying a curtain rod into the house and on a whim, pretended it was a rifle. A bloodcurdling scream came out of my mouth, and then I began laughing, which soon turned into tears. It was as if no time had passed." She said that the perceived gun was a "trigger", in a truer sense of the word than might have been intended, that took her right back to her previous experience.

Another caregiver, whose daughter had been

sexually abused by a family member and then started hurting herself with destructive behaviors, shared a similar story about her own PTSD: "I began home-schooling my daughter in order to make sure she could have a lot of time for therapy and was safe every moment of the day. I was working my way through guilt and overwhelm and went outside to sit by the lake. A neighbor friend came by to check in and walked up behind me and said hello. I screamed as if I was being attacked. I then erupted in nervous laughter before I broke into an uncontrollable sob. I had no control of my physical or emotional responses. It was only then that I knew something was going on with me."

For those suffering from PTSD, various physical symptoms such as headaches, tingling or numbness in the extremities, or tightness or burning in the chest may occur.

I personally experienced physical symptoms one morning when I awoke with such tightness, pressure, and burning in my chest that I thought I was having a heart attack. This was long after Stephen was safely back home, had lost thirty-five pounds, and was well on his way to a healthful, more vibrant life. Then the nightmares followed. There were vivid visions of Stephen having another heart attack, and they felt as real as my actual experience. In those dreams, my Beloved did not survive—and I would awaken trembling and fearful. Then my anxiety often lasted through the morning, and even sometimes well into the afternoon.

However, despite the hardships associated with PTSD, there is help! For example, "The Trauma Tool Kit: Healing PTSD From The Inside Out" by Susan Peace Banitt, LCSW, is a powerful guidebook using healing modalities such as yoga, meditation, hypnotherapy, acupuncture, nutrition, naturopathic treatment and much more, that can help manage PTSD.

In severe cases of PTSD, thoughts of suicide may enter your mind, and you should not be embarrassed or ashamed of this. It might seem like an escape from a world where you feel unsafe or have no control over traumatic things happening. If you have had a thought of suicide or are struggling and haven't reached out, please know there is help. Please call your local suicide hotline, or call 1-800-273-TALK (8255), 911, your therapist, or a local hotline that fits your situation. You can find the exact number with a quick search on Google or in the Yellow Pages.

Shocking You While Shocking Myself

Some of the extreme reactions I experienced as a result of my short-term caregiving may be shocking to you when you read about them. It shocked me to live them and the effects lasted far beyond my husband's recovery. I am sharing them to hopefully comfort you, and so you hopefully won't feel alone or ashamed if you have similar reactions.

Most people undergo serious stress in normal, daily living situations. This is something we all have to learn to manage and navigate through. But what I didn't realize then, but do now, is that as a wife, woman, partner, mother, and caregiver who watched her husband basically die twice while suffering a heart attack, I had instantly and simultaneously been introduced to four major types of stress: emotional, physical, psychological, and spiritual. Financial stress is also often heaped into the mix for caregivers due to medical bills for the patient and likely loss of work. So I had become upset, distressed, physically exhausted, worried, nervous, anxious and anything but Zen-like. I also felt confused, ashamed, and as if I had to hide my real feelings.

There were many things I could have done at the time to help myself heal and calm my emotions. For instance, there were spiritual practices I routinely used on an average day to center myself. But when I needed them the most, I dropped them, falsely rationalizing that I didn't have the time.

It's true you may not have time for your normal exercise class or that relaxing round of golf, but you can fit in these ten calming practices...

Taking The Time To Heal And Become Whole

1. Breathe. Take a deep breath and close your eyes. Imagine you are standing on the beach looking at the ocean. Breath deeply. Feel the warmth of the sun on your face, smell the ocean air. Breath deeply again. Feel love expand from your center to surround you. Remind yourself you are safe. Take one more deep breath and then open your eyes.

2. Make a ritual out of brewing yourself a cup of tea. With each sip feel the warmth comfort you. Think pleasant thoughts.

3. Write in a journal.

4. Do some yoga postures, bend, stretch, breath, feel the stress and negative energy leaving your body.

5. Remind yourself to be as gentle, forgiving, and loving to yourself as you are to others.

6. Light a candle and pray. Set an intention of

what your life will look like. When you blow out the candle see your intention going out into the universe and your prayers being answered.

7. Light some sage, walk through your space, and bless it with protection, love, and peace.

8. Close your eyes and meditate on the center of your being. Feel the precious core of your being. See and feel a loving white light expand from within to outside of your body. Feel the energy surround you and know you are safe, loved, and protected. Try to do this restful mind practice twice daily for ten to twenty minutes each time.

9. Joyfully prepare an organic, nurturing, delicious meal for yourself and your loved ones.

10. Take a bath or a shower. Water is extremely cleansing and meditative. Wash any stress or negative energy down the drain. It is said that visualizing your dreams while you are in water amplifies them to the universe. Saying a prayer while you are in water is a megaphone to heaven.

And here is a Big Free Easy Bonus! Talk to others. Healing begins when we speak our truth... and it gives others permission to do the same.

These simple actions take only moments and send a powerful healing message to our subconscious. How silly I was to think I didn't have the time when I needed them the most. But I learned and now continue to practice these techniques for mindfulness. The one thing I did do was speak the truth of my experience to the world. And how incredibly healing and honoring it has been to do so.

CHAPTER SEVEN

Speaking And Hearing It Like It Is

"It takes two to speak the truth: one to speak, and another to hear". ~Henry David Thoreau

As you move through your caregiving role, it is vital you have friends, support group members, or family members you can lean on and talk to. Understanding that you are not alone while being able to hear from others who have successfully moved through a caregiving journey, or are currently in one, will serve as a bridge over choppy waters for you.

For me, the gym and my friends in it became a great source of comfort and stress release. I also shared my experience with family members, friends, neighbors, workout buddies, my hair stylist, strangers at the dog park, and my favorite grocery store checkers. Basically, anyone who would listen.

I was surprised, and continue to be daily, by how many of my friends and new acquaintances have their own caregiving stories. They get loud and expressive in telling about their experiences, and seem to flash right back to the sounds, smells, colors, overwhelm, frustration, and exhaustion they went through. It became clear to me too that talking about my experience gave them the opportunity to release theirs as well. And I heard them. We weren't alone! We laughed. We bonded. We became a gang. And learned together that many times a tragedy or challenging time in life uncovers a hidden miracle.

My friend Leann shared: "When my husband broke his leg, I wanted to break his other leg many times!" she laughingly confessed. She admitted too that a few of her great moments of comedic relief were when she chuckled to herself about her self proclaimed "Kathy Bates" moments. In the film Misery, Annie Wilkes (Kathy Bates) breaks Paul Sheldon's (James Caan's) legs with a sledgehammer. I wince just thinking about that scene.

My friend vented about carrying trays upon trays of meals up and down the stairs to and from her husband, and all of the extra duties she took on while attempting to keep up with full-time work, household chores, extended family duties, and raising their young children. She also lovingly talked about how their challenging experience ended up being a gift from God because prior to her husband's accident, they had grown slightly apart in their marriage due to the stresses of work and raising children. However, after the accident, during the caregiving period, she confessed that they grew a little further apart before eventually growing back closer than ever before.

"It was as if heaven looked down on us and said, 'I am going to fix this but first I have to break your husband's leg'," my friend explained, laughing heartily. "We now look upon that experience as a gift in our lives."

While caregiving can end up being a blessing, many of us are not prepared for the situation or the stress heading our way. The result can be that the needs of the caregiver might fall by the wayside, causing them to feel invisible and "in the dark," while the patient is in the spotlight, receiving the best of care and having every need met. So you can understand now that even small gestures and slight levels of awareness could make a big difference in the health of caregivers. Simply having someone ask a caregiver how they are doing, and recognizing what they are doing, can work small miracles. Tell this to those around you.

It would be life-changing if nurses, physician's assistants, doctors, and surgeons routinely asked each patient "who is your primary caregiver?" in an effort to provide the caregiver with more resources such as support group contacts, self-care guidelines, spiritual inspiration, stress reduction tips, and information about what to expect.

Oh, and handing out this book would be very smart, too! With the exception of local support group contacts (which can easily be found by entering your city and "caregiving support groups" in your computer search engine), it's all right here.

Providing this information would be invaluable in warding off some of the challenges caregivers experience, and assist them in balancing out the give-and-take energy between the caregiver and the patient.

The next chapter is another glimpse into some of those surprising reactions that erupted within me and moved through me with unexpected force. The stress I was experiencing tore down my physical and emotional self restraints, letting loose a torrent of painful feelings much like a wild river. Every feeling that had crusted at the bottom of my being rose to the surface, shocking us all—but most of all, me.

CHAPTER EIGHT

Woman Gone Wild

"Be wild; that is how to clear the river. The river does not flow In polluted, we manage that. The river does not dry up, we block it. If we want to allow it its freedom, we have to allow our ideational lives to be let loose, to stream, letting anything come, initially censoring nothing."
~Clarissa Pinkola Estés, Women Who Run With The Wolves: Contacting The Power Of The Wild Woman

During the first few days when Stephen was in the hospital, before I found my caregiving posse and resumed meditative practices, I was aware of my body trembling as if shivering in sub-zero temperatures. It was only later that I realized I was releasing deep emotion, exhaustion, adrenaline, and fear. And a simmering anger which popped up briefly while he was in the hospital and then made a few more regular appearances after he returned home.

For awhile, I had no tolerance for Stephen not listening to me. I was going to make sure this man stayed alive and improved his health, so I made it clear that he would no longer have much room to budge, flinch, or refuse anything I recommended in his best interest. At all.

But there is some history that led me to these stern, what I now refer to as "Nurse Ratchet" or "Feeling Like Strangling The Patient," moments. For years, I had been concerned—truly worried, actually—about Stephen's health and would often have "pep talks" with him about joining a gym, exercising more, and eating healthier. His daughters were concerned too and would often come to me in private, anxious about their father's well-being. These talks were always met with resistance from Stephen, and dismissed as if I was being foolish and didn't have a reason in the world to be concerned. As time went on I became increasingly worried.

So after experiencing the horrid night of Stephen's heart attack, it was as if someone new showed up inside of me. She was a stern woman, and all about the business of keeping the patient alive.

In the days when I was fearful that my best friend, partner, and husband would have a heart attack, I imagined that if he were fortunate enough to survive, I would be filled with gratitude and immense love, with nothing else squeezing its way in. But other emotions and reactions were definitely squeezing their way in, quite often surprising me with their intensity.

What was most difficult in the beginning was feeling so apart from my partner. Stephen almost died and left us—and he promised that wouldn't happen for a long, long time. Then, during his recovery, my stable, intelligent, communicative husband seemed to be off in a drug-induced "la-la land," with no clear sign of a return. True, he wasn't really gone. But he wasn't completely "back," either.

Eventually, I would be comforted by caregiving acquaintances who shared similar stories of their own. But at that time I felt alone and missed the man who I knew as my partner prior to his heart attack. I also could not help but think of those caregivers whose partner or family member was suffering from long-term or terminal cancer, dementia, or Alzheimer's, and my heart ached for them.

Was my husband's visit to "la-la land" a vacation he intentionally went on? No. Was it the painkilling drugs that helped transport him? Yes. Was the fact that his heart stopped four times affecting the synapses within his brain? Probably. Were the new medications that he was taking adding to all of his fogginess? No doubt. Thankfully, in time, this all would recalibrate and I would get my beloved partner back in better shape than ever.

But initially, my adverse reactions were beginning to shock me more and more because they did not accurately represent who I felt I was or how I lived my life on a daily basis. My negative emotions and responses were puzzling to me especially since I knew how blessed we were to still have Stephen with us.

For example, on the third morning Stephen was in the hospital after his heart attack and surgery, I spoke to him on the phone while I was in the market at 6:00 am getting groceries for all of our family who had just flown home. "I am so glad everyone is there for you," he chirped cheerfully, a little high on painkillers. Yes, I agreed, it was great to be surrounded with loved ones after such a traumatic time. But it wasn't a party at home and now that he was through the worst of it and in the clear, I wanted my partner to understand a little of what I was going through.

So I started to share what the experience had been like for me. I had been terrified. I was exhausted and still hadn't slept or eaten very well. My body was suffering bouts of the trembles almost as if I was trying to literally "shake" the images I saw that night. But it was no use. They were stuck in my mind—and probably would be forever. Stephen's only reply was to repeat how great it was that everyone was home to help me, and how wonderful it was for both of us to be surrounded by family. Again I agreed, but I also became upset, feeling angry and like I was invisible and alone. I wanted him to not be so removed from what I was going through.

I tried to reiterate that I hadn't slept and that I was the one in the market at 6:00 a.m. shopping for the family. I attempted to relay that this wasn't a carefree family reunion and there was now lots more work to do at home. He attempted to talk over me, saying that he didn't understand why I was so upset, that he was just glad everyone was home to help me, and how great it was that we were all together.

"Seriously? Who are you?" I wondered. And eventually there I was, nearly shouting into my cell phone in aisle number twelve in front of the fruit juice, just trying to be heard. He interrupted and yelled, "You can't upset my heart!"

Upset his heart? What about my heart! What about the hearts of our family and friends and what they had gone through? To say that this nightmare had jolted some of them would be a huge understatement. Never mind his precious "you can't upset my heart" heart! In that moment, if I could have reached through the phone and strangled his recovering little neck, I would have!

Within one short week after watching my husband have a heart attack and almost die, I felt qualified to appear on the television show Snapped. Little did I know that I would remain a candidate for Snapped for a few more months to come. At the time, it hadn't even entered my mind that something had triggered my own over-the-top reactions.

I also wasn't conscious that my security had been shaken loose, leaving me feeling, and on occasion behaving, like a wild woman with emotions raging up from the depths of my being. Though Stephen had miraculously come through, for me, it felt as if I was still in survival mode. There in the market, after hanging up with my husband following a very uncomfortable phone call, I took a deep breath and realized that this period of my life was going to continue to be about Stephen for quite some time... as well it should.

I looked at the tomato juice and wondered where the vodka was. As I checked out in the express aisle, the clerk—who was now a friend, my having shopped at that particular market for many years—asked me why I looked so depleted. Her kind response to my explanation left me feeling grateful. "When my husband had cancer, I felt I'd lost my partner. I became scared and angry at the same time," she said. "Just give Stephen some time. He'll come back and be healthier and even more present than ever. You think this phase will last forever, but it won't."

Seriously? Does this happen in a supermarket before the sun even comes up?

I realized in that moment that many caregivers go through similar exhaustion and feelings of being alone, but their loved one doesn't come home. They experience death and loss at the end of their caregiving journey. After talking with my grocery cashier friend, I couldn't wait to get to the hospital to hug my husband and tell him that I was sorry.

In just a few moments, my checker friend had just become a valuable, comforting resource. I will mention again that there is no better resource than turning to caregivers who are experiencing, or who have experienced, what you are going through. Of course, I had no way of knowing that my food-check friend was in that category—which is a great reason for sharing with just about anybody who you think will listen, and certainly with anyone who asks. People care, they really do.

My dental hygienist also opened up to me after she learned of Stephen's heart attack. She said she was astounded by her own reaction when her husband had a stroke the year before. She said at first she didn't believe her husband when he called to tell her that he'd suffered a stroke while playing a game of racquetball. She mentioned that he was only in his forties and tended to be dramatic when it came to illness. She suggested he buck up and get back to work, and then was shocked later by how much more incensed she became with him when she realized his health condition turned out to be real. "He was supposed to take care of me and help with our four kids. Instead, it was now all about him. I was mad as hell, but stuffed it all down, embarrassed and ashamed. I had to call his mom to come and help, and even that frustrated me. I became really uncomfortable at a time when someone was supposed to be helping me become comfortable. These feelings scared me and I didn't feel like myself at all."

I told her I understood. Instead of being that grateful woman that I imagined I would be when my husband lived through a heart attack, I became someone I didn't even recognize. My caregiving friends and I slowly came to realize, each on our own terms, that we weren't bad humans simply because negative reactions were moving through us.

Please know that you aren't, either, if this has been true for you, or if it should happen to be in the future. By letting go and allowing our authentic feelings and reactions to exist no matter what they look like, we can move through challenging times more smoothly. For me personally, this meant not only recognizing but fully accepting, the wild, stern, and sometimes controlling woman within.

WHEN YOU FEEL LIKE STRANGLING THE PATIENT

CHAPTER NINE

Nurse Ratchet

"If Mr. McMurphy doesn't want to take his medication orally, I'm sure we can arrange that he can have it some other way." ~Nurse Ratchet in the film One Flew Over The Cuckoos Nest

My darling husband jumped fully into his role as Jack Nicholson—think both Cuckoo's Nest and Something's Got To Give—taking exercise laps around the hospital with his gown open in the back, while shuffling along in his worn-out slippers with a genuine smile spread across his entire face.

Yes, "Jack" was loving his new lease on life and thoroughly enjoying the impromptu family reunion, the extra love and all of the attention. And perhaps the painkilling drugs a little bit too! Whereas I quickly jumped into the role of Nurse Ratchet. I would pop in each morning just in time to meet another adorable, young nurse tending to my husband's every care and need. (Well, not *every* need. If so, I am sure he would still be living at the hospital.)

After standing there watching his pillows being
fluffed and repositioned, while hearing his careful
direction, "Well, no... if you could just, uh, move it
to the left and down a little bit," thereby extending
the fluffing process, I (Nurse Ratchet) would
interrupt and order "Jack" out of bed for another
exercise stroll around the hospital to speed up the
regaining of his independence.

In retrospect, I knew my husband was in dire pain

with bruised ribs, and, of course, I was grateful for the doctors and nurses who took such professional care of him. But his patient status scared me. I already wanted Stephen back to normal and was going to do everything I could to move along the process.

After five days in the hospital, Stephen was scheduled to come home. It was my stepdaughter, Tabitha, who told everyone in the family that his regaining any independence was going to take a while and that the full burden would fall on "Nonna's" shoulders. (Nonna is Italian for grandmother and the name our children and granddaughters call me.)

Say what?

Come again?

Bless Tabitha for bringing it up, but once again I hadn't realized what I was in for.

I was more than anxious to get a good night's sleep due to my husband sleeping next to me again. I was ready to relax and process with him all that we had been through, with everyone going "bye-bye" and returning to a sense of normal in own their lives. As much as I loved them all and was grateful for their love and support, I desperately needed some time with my husband, home alone with some quiet in the house, so that he and I could fully recover. And I am sure they did too.

We were all ready to resume a sense of normal.

This wasn't time for normal yet?

Now with distance, I can only reflect with gratitude on the many blessings we received. My husband, my children's stepfather, and my stepchildren's father, came home alive.

However, I wasn't thinking about the fact that my partner couldn't lift anything, or drive, or even walk well, much less that I would be taking over all of his household duties on top of mine for a while longer. I also wasn't thinking that almost everything in the grocery store has way too much sodium unless it's raw, organic, or fresh from the farm, and that cooking was going to take a whole new level of planning, time, care, and preparation.

Just because I was momentarily overwhelmed doesn't mean you have to be. In fact, there is an opportunity for you now in the following chapter. It is just for you with lists, guidelines, and things to understand upfront to protect your own well being in the midst of the caregiving process.

CHAPTER TEN

Dear Caregiver

"Love yourself first, and everything else falls in line. You really have to love yourself to get anything done in this world."

~ Lucille Ball

First, I want to say that I am so sorry for what you are going through, or for what you have already been through. You could still be raw, scared, and possibly even feeling somewhat numb. You are most likely without enough sleep or opportunity for you to process what is happening. Now (or soon) the patient will be coming home, if he or she hasn't already. Your duties have already increased and most certainly will multiply when they are back in the house. Understand that you will likely feel like a servant at times and won't be able to take care of yourself in all the ways that you should. But that is only for a while. It will change. For the time being, however, the main focus has been and will continue to be on the patient. Even so, here are three things to understand upfront to protect your own well being in the midst of the caregiving process:

#1 Expect to feel closer to your loved one (the patient) than you have ever been, and expect to feel, at other times, farther apart than you have ever been.

#2 You must make a real effort to care about yourself amidst all the care that surrounds the patient.

#3 Don't expect to be the perfect Florence (or Frank) Nightingale. You won't be.

Now, let's talk about the bottom line, your survival.

Ten Things Caregivers Must Not Fail To Do Daily To Survive

#1 Step up your nutrition. Eat organic (when possible), seasonal, local, whole foods, and grains. If this sounds daunting, just eat better than you normally do. Try to supplement with quality vitamins where you need extra support. Don't think "limiting". Think "replenishing". This also means drinking plenty of water regularly and reducing caffeine, alcohol and sugar consumption.

#2 Exercise. Do NOT omit exercise. Even if it is just walking around the grocery store before entering, or breathing in some fresh air while bending and stretching in your back yard, or taking a few flights of stairs at the hospital; fit it in.

#3 Accept help. Let me repeat: ACCEPT HELP! If friends offer to cook a few meals, walk your dog, run errands for you, sit with the patient while you go out etc., say "Yes, thank you!"

#4 Learn to say NO. Being a caregiver means recognizing your limitations and those of the patient.

#5 Reach out! Humans aren't wired to work solo. Trying to handle everything alone can lead to more stress and depression. Talk to friends or schedule an appointment with a counselor.

#6 Get out! Getting out of the house or the hospital, even for a short time, can do wonders. When the patient begins to reclaim parts of their daily routine, meet a friend for lunch or for an inspiring movie. If the patient is still in the hospital, eat your lunch outside, weather permitting.

Getting out of the house or hospital can boost inspiration, creativity, and most importantly, insight and clarity.

#7 Become aware of emotional triggers. Protect yourself by being present and aware when these triggers are activated. You can calm and center yourself by breathing and imagining the tension leaving your body while simply recognizing that the stirring inside is you reacting to one of your "hot buttons." More on this in Chapter Twelve.

#8 Unplug. For a small amount of time each day, unplug the computer, turn off the phone and go to a quiet room, or outside alone in nature, to breathe and just "be" for at least ten minutes. Everyone can take ten minutes for themselves daily in order to restore or just gather their senses. Everyone.

#9 Tell the patient something about yourself every day. As a caregiver, you check in with the patient and ask them how they are feeling and tend to their daily needs. In turn, tell them something they don't know about you or simply tell them how you are feeling. This will create intimacy and a more equal exchange of energy.

#10 Get sleep. Try taking a quick power nap during the day when the patient is resting. Getting horizontal and putting your feet up is extremely rejuvenating during stressful times. Lack of sleep will make everything worse and you will have a much harder time coping. Please check out Appendix A, A Caregiver's Survival Guide To Sanity for helpful tips on sleeping well.

#10A You get major bonus points if you can adopt some of the meditative practices described at the end of Chapter 6 and in Appendix A, A Caregiver's Survival Guide To Sanity. Write down your favorite ones and place this list on your desk, tape it to your refrigerator, or hang it on your bathroom mirror as a reminder that you can take a few moments for yourself each day.

I have come to realize that the most important thing we can do for our loved ones is to take the best possible care of ourselves. Above all, please remember in becoming a caregiver, one does not don a cape and attain magical superhuman powers. Be gentle with yourself.

One Powerful Thought You Must Have Daily

and The Three Reasons Why

Each day throughout your caregiving process, please understand that the best times of your life are still ahead of you, no matter how things look or feel in the moment. (Please see chapter Nineteen: Be Alive With Possibility! The Best Days Of Your Life Are Still Ahead Of You.) Being optimistic about the future will help you in three distinct ways:

#1 This regular thought pattern will reprogram the way we have been hypnotized by American society that has largely honored youth and ignored the wisdom, self-confidence, humility, valuable life skills and attributes that aging and life experience bring.

#2 This regular thought pattern will send a clear message to your subconscious that you are in charge of and inspired by your life.

#3 This regular thought pattern will become true for you because your positive energy will create opportunities, bring insights, and open doors to walk through.

Many people have discovered their dreams and lived their passions much later in life because they believed that they would. It makes sense that most great things in life—whether it is wine, cheese, art, music, or a garden—need a little seasoning and growing before they evolve into greatness.

Please know I have great respect for you and your journey in caring for another human being or beings. I count you among the secular saints of our time, before and beyond, who have been called to enrich their own lives simply by helping others. Bravo, brave friend. Bravo!

CHAPTER ELEVEN

Caregiving for a Terminally Ill Loved One

"A human life is a story told by God." ~Hans Christian Andersen

I write this chapter with my heart pounding and tears welling up. I imagine your sadness, urgency, pain, confusion, and feelings of abandonment. I also feel your need to distance yourself in one moment and the desire to reach out the next. I am so sorry, so dearly sorry. Perhaps the news you received was sudden and you just found out your loved one only has a certain number of days, weeks, or months to live. If so, your world has changed drastically.

It's as if you have just been served papers in the form of a sentence to a new life which you did not consciously agree to. You may be experiencing many different emotions and reactions within seconds of each other. You may feel immense love, disbelief, guilt, yearning, and then anger toward the very person (or terminal illness) you are grieving. If you have not yet felt these things, be aware that you might soon. On top of all of this, you will be dealing with your loved one who could be in shock, denial, or angry, sad, scared, terrified, and depressed.

I understand that this is an extremely sensitive time. If you need to skim over this part of this chapter (or any part of this book, for that matter) until you are ready, then please do so. You may also be living with strong hope and possibly even researching or trying alternative therapies so you may never have to read the material here. I understand that miracles exist.

What if the news of your loved one's terminal illness is not sudden? Today, with advances in medicine, having a loved one live with a terminal diagnosis for one to three to five years or more is common. This means the terminally ill patient and their family could live with death hanging over them for an extended period of time.

Throughout life, we get clues as to the direction in which our journey is headed. We also have dreams of what our future will look like. Then a terminal diagnosis blows in and all of that vanishes. The Earth suddenly feels gone beneath our feet and as if a wind is sweeping us away. When everything we thought would be there for us evaporates, we are left to surrender, trust, and be. So your job is to just be here in the best way you can, slowly taking one step at a time.

The challenges that individuals and families face when a loved one is dying are complex. Even loving partners or family members may find their relationships in jeopardy as a result of the new lifestyle placed upon them. It is important to take time to be there for each other and to not judge the other's feelings or judge how each individual is handling the situation. However, helping your terminally ill loved one can also add great value to your relationship because terminal illness strips away anything false or materialistic in life, and makes room for the soul and spiritual essence of who you are to be brought to the surface. It is also a time for giving unconditionally. Helping your loved one's self-esteem is especially important here. Talking of their accomplishments and the love that surrounds them is extremely comforting. Often during this period, the patient's body is breaking down, which can feel like a degrading process to them. The once well-oiled machine is no longer, and this can be both confusing and depressing.

As I write this, a dear friend's father is dying of brain cancer. I hesitate to write the word dying because at this moment he is living with brain cancer. It appears that he and his family have mainly been in the midst of the "unreality" stage. The "unreality" stage is a state of almost complete numbness. It is a time when the patient and family members hope for miracles. When they still talk about "when Dad is all better", and make plans for the distant future.

I recall this stage when I was by my grandmother's side for the last few months of her life. I knew she was leaving us soon and had to encourage other family members to come and be by her side because they didn't believe she was close to leaving us. Understandably, no one wanted to acknowledge or believe she was.

The next stage is almost like entering into a space of peace, grace, freedom, and joy. Families and loved ones talk about taking magical vacations, planning drives to the beach, having picnics in special places, and arranging for celebrations. My friend's father, who I mentioned above, is slowly entering this new stage. Talks have begun about taking a trip to Ireland and Scotland with their children and grandchildren. Terminal illness can seem to give "the okay" to take that magical vacation you have always dreamed of but never felt quite right spending the money on. Creating this space for joy is so important as it can fuel the patient, family members, and loved ones for perhaps the most taxing stage, that of dealing with practical concerns. Such as those surrounding the physical needs of the patient, finances, and death, along with the ongoing demands of the entire family.

Don't Be Surprised By Anger

Anger may arise out of fear and be directed at God, the universe, or life in general. The very real fact that your loved ones time with you is finite, long before you were prepared to accept that notion, is sure to stir up some intense feelings. Hostility may arise out of disappointment, confusion, and even animosity if you believe your loved one's terminal illness has been created by self-neglect. You may even find yourself turning towards a substance or situation to comfort you. But do not sit in judgment of yourself. You are doing the best you can. Try your best to make healthy choices to reduce your stress. It will all get easier as your circumstances shift.

Being Angry Does Not Mean You No Longer Love The Patient

I have a friend Jerilyn who lost her mother to breast cancer. Her mom was the president of a university, held a Ph.D. in microbiology, and was active in the funding for and the start-up of a high tech health facility, the Martha Anne Dow Center for Health Professionals. Ironically, the building houses state of the art equipment for mammography, radiology and ultrasound. Her mom also was the recipient of numerous awards for her role in the community. Why am I giving you all of her impressive credentials? Because even though Jerilyn's mother found out that she had a terminal illness, she chose to not tell her family about it nor to seek treatment for her condition.

The family only found out after she collapsed at work. Then, after a few months she passed away. Five years later, my friend Jerilyn is still coming to terms with her mother's behavior and rather quick, self-propelled death. She often feels her mother's absence, like when her boys are playing baseball and wishes "grandma" could have experienced the joy of watching them grow up. She fluctuates between sadness, anger, confusion, and sorrow for not having been able to be there for her mother. Even though she understands at some level that her mother chose to suffer alone with breast cancer for over a year and never explained then why she had not told the family about her condition or sought treatment.

The point of the story is that for many people, dealing with a terminal illness feels like a very private matter. They may be scared and not want to heighten their fear by telling others—they may also not feel up to dealing with the reactions of their loved ones. Or they may not want to "burden" family and friends with their illness, preferring to "go it alone" until it is just not possible to do so anymore.

When we love someone, the first call of love is to respect their innermost decisions—especially about something as intimate as their own death, and their manner of dealing with it. So while it may be natural to feel angry or deeply disappointed about the choices they have made, your peace may be found in the knowledge that the one we love got to make their final major life decisions in the way that they wanted—and being "okay" with that can be our final gift to them.

There Is Hope

I am conscious that what you need is guidance and some understanding of what you might expect. I have ten concrete suggestions to help you right now:

#1 Please know that however you are feeling is what you are supposed to be experiencing to help you move through this journey. Allow your authentic emotions to run free as one of the hardest lessons to learn is unconditional love. Please begin with yourself.

#2 Read or re-read Chapter Ten, Dear Caregiver, in which I share ten things to do daily in order to survive.

#3 Get some expert resources in your hands and then ingest them when you are ready. Three powerful books I recommend are: Living With Death And Dying, by Elisabeth Kübler-Ross, M.D., Three Months: A Caregiving Journey from Heartbreak to Healing, by J. Dietrich Stroeh, and Saying Goodbye: How Families Can Find Renewal

Through Loss, by psychologists Barbara Okun and Joseph Nowinski.

#4 Seek refuge in a support group or pick up the phone and reach out to someone who has lived what you are going through. This will help you more than you know.

#5 Talk to your dying loved one. I mean, really talk. Tell them everything you've ever wanted to say. Tell them every reason you love them and list, as specifically as you can, every gift they ever gave you, and everything you have learned from them. This will help them to further understand how worthwhile their life was, and how they brought something of real meaning to others. Tell them what you most admire them for. Then, ask them if they would like to talk about their own dying; how it feels, what it means to them, what questions they may have—and, whether they would like someone to talk with who might bring them spiritual guidance during this time. Often patients will not specifically ask for this, but when offered, they may very much welcome the suggestion or idea. If they do want this spiritual guidance, please make sure it is someone who does not fill their heart with fear. You may wish to ask the patient, "What, if anything, do you believe happens after death?" This will tell you what kind of spiritual teacher, pastor, or minister to offer to bring in.

#6 Read to your dying loved one. Often, the ability of the terminally ill to see well enough to read, or to concentrate sufficiently, can be impaired. Offer to read a chapter at a time of their favorite book. Or, suggest a book they may wish to hear you read from. (A wonderful book that has brought comfort to many people is HOME WITH GOD in a Life That Never Ends, by contemporary spiritual author Neale Donald Walsch). If your loved one can still read comfortably, then watch inspiring movies together and talk, tell stories.

#7. Practice the art of simply Being With. As humans, we are hard wired to produce and create. Something we have to learn is being still. In this space, we can witness and just be. Sitting, just sitting and not talking, by your loved one's side sends a huge message of support, stability, and love. An idea I used while the children were growing up was a "safe room." If there was fighting or struggling to express themselves or any feelings of exasperation, they could leave and go sit alone safely in this room. The only action another family member could take was to enter the room and sit quietly next to them. This process helped melt walls and frustrations.

#8. Give your loved one a chance to "confess." And practice Non-Judgmental Listening. Many dying people have things they want to "get off their chest." They may not be particularly religious, and so the idea of "confessing" to a priest or minister may not fit their paradigm. Yet, they may wish they had someone to just "offload" to. Often deep and very meaningful conversations can be ignited by asking your loved one, "Would you tell me your favorite memories and the most joyous experiences of your life? I would love to hear the stories!" And then, some time later, perhaps: "Do you have anything that you wish you could say or reveal—any regrets and sadness or anything you'd like to just 'get off your chest' with someone, with total privacy and a sacred oath of secrecy?" Sometimes patients will chuckle and say, "No, not really." But sometimes patients will say, " I am so glad, so grateful, that you asked me that. Yes...there is something...." And then they will tell you. You are giving them a chance to finish their own Unfinished Business. And the words they want to hear, then, are simply: "You are forgiven." Not "I forgive you," but the more neutral, "You are forgiven."

#9 Take time for yourself. Allow others to spend time with your loved one as you take some much-needed opportunities to be alone and refuel. Treat yourself to a massage, spend time with friends, walk in nature, prepare (or order out) some delicious healthful meals, or watch an inspiring film. Or read a poignant book. One of the most poetic memoirs I have read that is about being by a loved one's side with a terminal illness is What Remains: A Memoir of Fate, Friendship and Love, by Carole Radziwill.

#10 Give yourself a chance to "confess." Sit down with someone you trust; a clergy member, a friend, or a professional counselor who will practice Non-Judgmental Listening. Many caregivers themselves have things they need to "get off their chest."

At times like these, our friends and loved ones are drawn to us, so please accept their help and loving guidance. Try also looking online for other guidance and see what speaks to you. Trust your instincts and go with them.

A point of awareness for caregivers looking after a loved one who is terminally ill is to understand that someday you will experience a sense of rebirth and freedom just as the patient might. It may occur through this very experience of being by a loved one's side as they transition. Because caregiving for a loved one opens us up to many gifts. Expect them to show up. Love will surround you so please wrap it around you and carry it with you like an old soft blanket.

In closing, from The Wheel Of Life, A Memoir Of Living And Dying, by Elisabeth Kübler-Ross, M.D.: "When we have passed the tests we were sent to Earth to learn, we are allowed to graduate. We are allowed to shed our body, which imprisons our soul the way a cocoon encloses the future butterfly, and when the time is right we can let go of it. Then we will be free of pain, free of fears and free of worries....free as a beautiful butterfly returning home to God...which is a place where we are never alone, where we continue to grow and to sing and to dance, where we are with those we loved and where we are surrounded with more love than we can ever imagine."

CHAPTER TWELVE

Becoming Aware Of Triggers

"A trigger is a mirror to the fear and alarm that remain in the body." ~Yours truly

If down the road you react to a situation with all of the overwhelm and stress you had initially during a tragic time in your life, then you are experiencing an emotional trigger. As caregivers we can hold many triggers associated with needs in our lives such as balance, order, peace, freedom, love, attention, fairness, consistency, comfort, control, safety, fun, being valued and "seen" or witnessed in the world, and feeling respected and understood.

Triggers can be small, big, and varied. These triggers can plunge you instantly into the past, causing you to feel fearful or alarmed. You can, just as all of us can, learn to recognize, defuse, and release triggers that remain.

A trigger is a mirror to the fear and alarm that remains in the body. It is emotional and physical. A trigger can also seemingly take you instantly back to childhood. In a millisecond, your energy can shrink and you are reacting as if you are nine years old.

There are many ways to be triggered by an unresolved experience that remains in the body. Noticing when one of your triggers is being activated is a key point in moving through or even bypassing a negative situation. For instance, my caregiving friend whose husband broke his leg, had a severe reaction when a year later he had to go back into surgery to have pins and plates removed. She described her overwhelming feelings this way: "We were driving to the hospital and I just started sobbing, remembering all the meals, going up and down the stairs, the exhaustion, the overwhelm, the stress, and the extra work that was piled on me. The drive to the hospital triggered my body to react as if it was happening all over again. I was incredibly upset and it took quite a while for me to calm down and even understand what was happening."

I can relate and I am sure you can too. I recall my own huge, emotionally triggered response on Stephen's first evening home from the hospital. He refused to eat something while taking medication even though his doctor's and pharmacist's specific instructions were to take the medication with food as it could cause extreme nausea otherwise. Throwing up with bruised or broken ribs is not fun, but throwing up and taxing the heart when it needs to get stronger can cause another heart attack. Needless to say, that should be avoided. But still he refused to eat some crackers!

And I snapped. Mentally, physically, and emotionally, I flashed right back to all the times that he had not heard my intense concerns about his health and eating habits, which in turn had led to me having to experience him dying in front of my eyes, twice. So in my body it felt like it was happening all over again.

If only I could have recognized, while I was becoming increasingly upset, that just because Stephen wasn't "hearing me", it didn't mean he was going to collapse on the floor in front of me again. Unfortunately, the stored energy in my body reacted as if the heart attack was happening once more. If I could have caught myself in the moment by noticing that I was being "triggered", a signal would have been sent to my brain that this might not be as real as all the intense emotions I was feeling were leading me to believe, and my reaction could have been defused.

Another example of a trigger for me is that for a few months after Stephen returned home from the hospital, a full house equaled the energy drain, fear, and exhaustion I felt after Stephen had his heart attack. Though the situation wasn't really recurring, anytime we were going to have a full house, I reacted with the same overwhelm that I experienced during that initial time. And it remained that way until I had the opportunity to reframe the experience of having a full house as something joyful. That reframing eventually happened when family members came home after we all had enough rest and recovery and experienced a restful, enjoyable time together.

At some point during the caregiving process, opportunities will be presented to you for the disproportionate responses and triggers to fade away. Remember this though: healing has little to do with what happened in the past and everything to do with how you handle and perceive experiences going forward. Which means one of the keys to defusing and eventually releasing your triggers is to notice them.

If you notice yourself reacting to a trigger you can send a signal to your brain that the current moment might not be as real as all the emotions that are surging through are making you believe.

For example, we have various needs, and during certain times of caregiving, we might have gone long periods without those needs being met. If we feel ourselves reacting with intensity, we can take a moment to breathe and check in with ourselves. We can ask ourselves: "Am I reacting to this current situation too intensely because of my past experience?" We can step outside of the situation, rise above it, and then take the time to figuratively look down from ten thousand feet. It will still be there. It's not going anywhere. It just might be there for us to witness in a more gentle and non-threatening fashion.

Remember The Flight Attendant Rule For Survival

As a former flight attendant, we were always instructed to put our oxygen masks on first in the event of an emergency, or we would have been of no assistance to anyone else. So we must take excellent care of ourselves, or we won't be successful at trying to save, comfort, assist, or help those we love.

Let us pledge now, within the very core of our being, that our first responsibility is to ourselves. We can't be a caregiver for someone else if we destroy our own well-being and, honestly, our loved ones wouldn't want us to do that anyway.

CHAPTER THIRTEEN

Caregiver Stress Syndrome

"Welcome change as the rule, not the ruler."
~Dennis Waitley

The exhaustion, anger, financial pressure, and other negative outcomes of caregiving have created what is now known in the medical community as "Caregiving Stress Syndrome." This condition encompasses actual physiological and psychological maladies that result from the ongoing strain of caregiving for a loved one. A few of the caregivers I spoke with experienced some or all of the following symptoms: difficulty sleeping, fatigue, depression, anxiety, panic, memory problems, money problems, high blood pressure, migraines, and illness.

Caregivers can adversely impact their own health because they are more likely to neglect their physical and mental well-being due to their caregiving responsibilities. On top of that, many people do not recognize (until it is too late) this negative side of caregiving. So being very clear about this condition is critical if we are going to proactively make healthy choices for ourselves as caregivers.

We must expect change in life, but we do not have to let new circumstances control us. We can still feel empowered to make decisions. And remind ourselves that we have choices, while also recognizing our strengths as well as our limitations—doing so remains crucial in designing a life we want to live. Sometimes though we only come to know our limitations the hard way, such as through exhaustion or burnout. And you know what? That is entirely okay if, and only if, we listen to the message that the burnout is sending us and then take corrective action.

Let's recognize that while both long-term caregivers and short-term caregivers are at risk for caregiving stress syndrome, caregiving long term is a much more daunting task. I readily and lovingly acknowledge that I can't even imagine the emotional toll that long term caregiving can take, nor can I speak with any authority about caregiving a parent, a child, or a loved one who has a terminal illness or a disease such as Alzheimer's. I do, however, have friends, neighbors, and acquaintances who are doing so on a daily basis. So I reached out to them to try to understand what they are going through.

Long Term Caregiving & Caregiving The Chronically Ill

One famous couple, President and Mrs. Reagan, were dear friends of my husband Stephen's parents Armand and Harriett Deutsch. Stephen still ponders how difficult it must have been for Mrs. Reagan to care for her ailing husband for ten years when he didn't even know who she was or that he had ever been president. Theirs was a love affair that the world witnessed. Mrs. Reagan appeared stoic in her efforts to accept loss and forge ahead without her beloved's awareness, and eventually without his physical form by her side.

I can tell you also about a woman I spoke with named Sandy. She was caring for her husband who was in the hospital with Chron's syndrome, a chronic, inflammatory bowel disease. She mentioned that it can be painful and debilitating, and lead to life-threatening complications. She had spent many hours and days alone in the emergency and ICU waiting room with white knuckles. She shared: "What surprised me the most is the friends that don't return your calls and the family members that fade away. Some people don't know how to deal with situations that are uncomfortable. They don't know what to ask or say or do, so they go away."

When we enter into the role of caregiver, we find out who our real friends and loved ones are. They show up even when they don't know what to do or how to act and be. But sometimes that is all we need as caregivers — just to have someone sitting next to us.

I realize I said earlier that friends and loved ones do, indeed, sometimes "show up" even when nothing has been asked of them and they don't know what to do, or how to act or be. So I see that what I am saying now could seem contradictory. Well then, Is input from, and contact with, friends and loved ones helpful, wanted, and needed or not?

The answer is that, as in all things, it is a matter of discernment and discretion. And as a caregiver, one of your challenges will be to conduct this orchestra. To start with, you'll likely find it helpful to simply speak lovingly, clearly and precisely to your friends and loved ones, letting them know what could really be of help to you and how and when they might offer that assistance. Tell them, too, what will not help like phone calls after dark because they can't sleep and are feeling sad, etc. People will be grateful to have this kind of direction. In truth, everyone wants to do what they can, and they might not know what that is unless you tell them, thus helping them to help you.

And if some friends or loved ones do indeed seem to slip away because of their discomfort, do not be afraid to reach out when you have a moment or two, and contact them. Simply tell them the truth: "I know this may be uncomfortable for you, but now is the time I could really use you. I am feeling so alone in this. Could you call me or connect with me now and then, maybe once a week or so, just to 'check in'? It would feel so good to me to know that you've got my back. Could I ask you for this?"

Now I know that most people are not used to talking to others this way—much less directly asking for help so openly—but we all appreciate it so greatly when others speak to us this way. So you can feel assured that most other people will also be very happy to receive such honest, open communication from you that they are needed. Most people will receive this as a compliment, and respond accordingly.

Caregiving A Parent

Throughout our lives, we are usually identified by our roles: daughter, son, parent, wife, husband, mother, father. As our parents age, these roles often take on new meanings.

So often though there isn't a loving partner like Nancy Reagan to care for "Dad" (President Reagan) or a character like James Garner's ("Duke") who lovingly takes care of the love of his life, Gena Rowlands ("Allie") in the film The Notebook. Which means as the average lifespan of the population continues to increase, more and more baby boomers will find themselves assuming the role of a caregiver for their parents.

The result may be that we find ourselves as exhausted from caregiving a parent as a new parent might feel with the birth of their first child. The only difference is that exhaustion from new parenthood eventually eases, while one may experience the exhaustion of caregiving a parent daily, 24-hours a day, for many years. This exhaustion may persist even after the caregiver has moved their parent into a full-care senior facility or, most sadly, after they have passed on.

Caregiving is complicated enough. Caregiving a parent is beyond complicated, particularly when it is for an uncertain amount of time. It can place a great deal of strain on families and especially partnerships. If there is more than one family member available, taking care of an elderly parent should not be a one-person job. Many ruptures occur in families because one child may be willing to help while the other siblings are not willing to step up and do their share.

One of the firemen who saved Stephen's life later told me that he had just moved his mother into his family home to help care for her. He also mentioned that this new caregiving arrangement was causing some tension. The silver lining, he said, is that eventually many families become much closer because of their shared time together across generations.

We have a sweet neighbor, Ann, who worked with her husband to renovate their home so that her mother and small dog could move in with them. We often see Ann and her lovely mother walking their dogs past our home. They are a part of the sandwich generation, a wave of people who are now caring for their aging parents while also supporting their own children. Our neighbors have one older child at home, an adult child in college and now a mother at home.

At some point in time, it is important to stop and survey your current caregiving situation. Then create a strategy that will also help bring YOU hope and aid YOU as a caregiver.

Caregiving A Child

"Making the decision to have a child is momentous. It is to decide forever to have your heart go walking around outside your body."
~Elizabeth Stone

What if you are the parent of a child (adult or younger) with a chronic, fatal, or grave illness, or of a child who has just had a serious accident?

That question opens up an entirely new area of caregiving, one in which depression, overwhelm, and exhaustion are apt to befall the heartbroken parent.

While caregiving spouses might find it a little easier to vent because "the patient" is a peer, the circumstances dramatically shift when the patient is your parent or, most sensitively, your child. Worry, guilt, and helplessness are common but overwhelming feelings for a parent with a disease-stricken or badly injured child. Having something horrible happen to your children certainly can feel much worse than if it was happening to you, and many parents harbor guilt that such awfulness befell their child instead of them.

To illustrate this, I'll tell you about my friend Lana. Her adult daughter lost some of her fingers due to Compartment Syndrome, which is a life-threatening condition. It is defined as " the compression of nerves, blood vessels, and muscle inside a closed space (compartment) within the body."

My friend's life drastically changed when her adult

daughter was stricken. Living in another state, Lana temporarily left her husband and her life behind and moved back in with her ex-husband for almost five months to care for their daughter. By that time her daughter was dealing with not only the loss of some of her fingers, but possibly her livelihood as a nurse as well.

Sometimes though an adult child who is the patient might resent the caregiving if it takes the form of extra "mothering" or "fathering," even if the caregiving is helpful and perhaps needed. That's what Lana encountered and eventually came back home. She also had her own heavy heart to deal with, compounded by the financial strain of having to help cover hospital bills and living expenses for her daughter. Even now, when Lana attempts to help her adult daughter move forward, she is often told by her daughter to stop "over-mothering". Dealing with the tornado of various emotions and feelings has been a challenge for them, as well as for the families that surround them. It has been helpful to Lana to remember that she cannot control everything that happens either to her or to her loved ones. And as a part of that self awareness she has had to learn to accept her daughter's choices to move forward or not.

On the outside, in exercise class, and in life in general, Lana is upbeat and the epitome of laughter and fun. However, during her caregiving period she often felt the need to "take to her bed," which in her very southern style translates as spending time alone processing what she and her family were going through. Both Lana and her adult daughter had much to cope with while a new way of "being" had been born in both of their lives.

Update: Lana and her daughter remain focused on the mini-miracles that appeared throughout their journey and how those beacons give them hope, perspective, and inspiration for the future. Lana's solution to help her daughter move through, and let go to a certain extent, was to focus on the fact that "My daughter is an adult and will learn to navigate the circumstances of her own life as she gains strength from within and from those who love her."

It may take some time before we are able to gain enough distance to witness the gifts in our own caregiving journey. The more practiced we are in self care, while embracing both the genuine sorrows and joys of caregiving, the more we will be able to gain this clearer perspective. One moment of clarity for me came when my dear friend Jeanette, ninety-two years young, looked into my curious brown eyes with her wise, crystal-clear, blue ones, grabbed my face, and said, "Embrace your sorrows and your sadness as deeply as you embrace your joys." She taught me that even the darkest hours of our lives contain gifts for our evolution as human beings.

This was a woman who had buried two husbands and one son. A woman with a loving family and a life rich beyond what I could describe here. The role of caregiver was one she inhabited more than once in her lifetime, and became ill and temporarily run down because of it.

Jeanette said, "The key in getting back up is embracing our sorrow fully, while knowing faith will move us through." She also understood something very valuable: "Being a caregiver was just one of the roles in my life, a small part of who I am."

Don't Turn Caregiving Into An Identity

We all know and probably love someone who identifies with being a victim. The behaviors that surround such a weak perception will never fill the seemingly bottomless reservoir needing love. So just as important as it is to not turn victim-hood into an identity or a lifelong career, it applies also for caregiving.

Jeanette's caregiving role did not define her. Among other things, she had been a Women's Air Force Service Pilot (WASP) —the first women in history to fly American military aircraft during World War II. She had also been a ski instructor, windsurfer, professor, doctor of theology, mother, wife, artist, student of spirituality, perpetual student of life, and so much more.

It was clear to me that it was Jeanette's attitude and response toward the events of her life, not the events themselves, that propelled her forward and enabled her to accomplish so much, regardless of what happened to her. (There is a marvelous description of how to make this work for you in your life in the book When Everything Changes, Change Everything, by Neale Donald Walsch. It talks about how events have nothing to do with the reality in which one resides—and it discusses how to use what he calls the Mechanics of the Mind to create the reality that you wish.) So as caregivers, our attitude towards our caregiving situation, not the caregiving situation itself, will help determine our quality of life.

When Caregiving Makes Us Ill

Let's acknowledge that watching a loved one deteriorate is a terrible emotional drain on the caregiver too. And the caregiver often never fully gets to rest due to feeling the need to be on alert at all times. For example, a friend, Lynne, shared her story with me:

"I had so much responsibility taking care of my husband, Ney, who was recovering from quadruple bi-pass surgery while also developing Alzheimer's. At the same time, I was pressured by my strong desire to continue working full time to support my son so he could get a college education.

"After Ney had passed on, my son obtained his degree. I, however, found myself unable to work. Ultimately, I had to take an unexpected early retirement because of my own failing health. The caregiving had simply drained me and I had become very ill.

"When I think back to what I had gone through and to all that I had accomplished, I am so proud that I did it. You have to do the best you know how in that moment. Now I have to learn to give to myself all the love that I gave to both of them."

Lynne says she gets inspired by watching Spiritual Cinema Circle films and seeing how, against all odds, others are having the courage to face up to their own personal responsibilities. She says she encourages others to be very mindful of their own self care and self-love in order to ward off illness.

Another friend, Tom, who I met at a film festival in Sun Valley, Idaho, had been caring for both of his parents for over eight years. At the time we met I had no idea that this handsome actor/producer was heavily immersed in his own unique path of caregiving. He wrote me almost a year later, "I write as I prepare to see a doctor tomorrow about a circulation issue causing tingling in my feet. This odd event popped up when I was caregiving my parents for four years. It has been eight years now since I left Hollywood to care for my parents, which has limited my work and now caught me in a gap with no insurance. My Dad has now passed on, and Mom, at 77, has many more issues."

More caregivers like Tom and so many others should be recognized and appreciated for what they have gone through and for what they have given up while caring for loved ones. Receiving a small dose of support through a simple mention or moment of recognition from another soul could be just the unexpected boost they need.

CHAPTER FOURTEEN

Support Is Essential

"With providence as your guide and with a determination to just keep moving, your life will unfold as it should." ~ Morgan Freeman

Receiving support and having determination are essential in life, but especially so while taking on the role as a caregiver.

When some of my caregiving friends mentioned that a doctor, nurse, family member, or friend had pulled them aside and asked how they were doing, they shared with me that it instantly changed their perspective. The shift went from dark to light. This simple act of someone taking the time to genuinely ask how they were doing made these caregivers feel "seen" and cared for themselves.

One friend whom I will call Robert said: "When I brought my father (who was dying of cancer) into the office, his doctor noticed the bags and circles under my eyes and pulled me out into the hall to ask me how I was doing. I started crying because I couldn't believe he cared, or that someone understood." That same doctor urged Robert to join a support group and took the time to help him locate one. "The support group changed my life and my perspective." In looking back on that period when he was a caregiver, Robert told me the support group helped him get in touch with not only his grief but also with his deep appreciation for the experience to have been there for his dad. "It has been over a year since my dad passed. It was an honor to be with him. We had much time to talk about life and what was important, and today I am living a better life because of the time I shared with my father."

Thanks to online support too, caregivers can easily be directed to caregiving books, caregiving blogs and websites, and to local "in person" support groups.

Another caregiving friend echoes Robert's view about the value such support groups can bring to a caregiver's experience, assuring their continued well-being and health: "I began to fall apart physically and mentally watching my wife fade away. What good would it do her or I if I fell apart? Who would take care of her? I became alarmed, then talked to my doctor, and she helped me find a support group. The friends in this new group kept me from falling into depression and illness. People care. You just have to be brave and reach out. You can't do it alone."

As a caregiver, it is important to understand that even though you are temporarily giving up some time in your life, you have not lost power or control over your life. Your caregiving moment could, in fact, be an opportunity to declare yourself anew in the world; an opportunity to redesign what you want the rest of your life to look like going forward. It's relatively easy to declare who we are when things are rosy, but proclaiming who we are during rough times is a powerful point in life. As Jim Rohn says, "We all have two choices. We can go about living or we can design a life."

Keep Support Simple With Caring Bridge

www.caringbridge.org

(And other similar sites such as www.lotsahelpinghands.com)

I remember back in English 101 when my professor first stressed the K.I.S.S. principle in writing: Keep It Simple Stupid! I have come to find out, the hard way, that the K.I.S.S. formula also works in the land of caregiving. If only I had known! I hadn't heard about Caring Bridge (or other similar sites) until long after Stephen's heart attack, surgery, and recovery.

Caring Bridge is a nonprofit resource that helps organize and simplify communications between caregivers, family members, and friends of the patient through free, private websites. Whether a Caring Bridge patient site is used for posting messages of support, for providing information about the patient's well-being, and even coordinating the delivery of meals, it is a stress-free way to communicate and keep everyone in the loop the healing journey.

In Support Of Ourselves

Knowing "who you are" not only while you caregive, but in life in general, is one of the best assets you can ever have. Being able to proclaim "who you are" when the chips are down will require utter vulnerability and complete courage, but the universe will always honor your declaration.

CHAPTER FIFTEEN

Heavenly Inspiration

"It's okay, honey. I was just talking to the cornfield". ~Ray Kinsella in Field of Dreams.

As caregivers, we often find ourselves searching for hope and understanding, and often can find it in the most common of ways. Whether it is from God, Jesus, Buddha, heaven, nature, or those around us, it's always there.

And 'the Voice' isn't always subtle. In the film Field Of Dreams, it was "the Voice" in the cornfield that spoke to Ray Kinsella. His wife Annie skeptically teased him, "Hey, Ray, what if 'the Voice' calls while you're gone?" "Take a message," he replies in a sincere and matter-of-fact manner.

In real life, "the Voice" that speaks to you might come from your grocery checker, your mechanic, a waitress, a neighbor, a dear friend, your doctor, fitness instructor, or a family member. "The Voice" might also speak through a flash of insight, a dream, or simply a feeling that floats in.

During my husband's ordeal, my interactions at our neighborhood grocery store were beyond healing for me. While my family and friends remained the constant voices of reason and heavenly channeling for me, the illuminating encounters I had with others while doing our weekly marketing surprised me the most. Those moments happened often, were varied, and always occurred when I needed them the most. Here are just a few examples of the wisdom my friendly checkers and neighbors imparted to me:

"My husband had a heart attack 25 years ago while he was in his forties. Your husband will be around for a long time, too. Don't worry."

"You do know that Stephen came back because of his love for his family don't you?"

"It wasn't Stephen's time. Just time for a massive wake-up call is all."

"Stephen wasn't listening to you. But he is sure listening now, isn't he?"

"Now it is time to take care of you, Lauren. This is your wake-up call, too."

Stephen's heart attack actually did become a very specific wake-up call for me as well as for others close to us. Tragedies and health scares can often remind us of "the gift of being alive" as well as many other gifts such as recognizing the kindness and the generosity of spirit that flows from the human heart. During a tragedy or health scare, we are also often awakened to the fact that material things aren't the real treasures in life. The real treasures are the ones we carry with us in our hearts; love, connection, awareness, and a helpful and grateful spirit. Those treasures can bring unbridled freedom.

My friend Lana, whose daughter lost some of her fingers due to compartment syndrome, spoke of a special "angel" friend who generously helped them out during a frightening time full of uncertainty. This "angel" provided stability, comfort and a sense of knowing that they weren't alone:

"We needed to get to a larger hospital closer to home to continue with Harriet's healing. She had to be flown on a medical jet. It was very expensive, and we didn't have the money at that time. A friend became our angel and made it happen without our asking. That was a miracle."

Then there at the hospital in their hometown, a special nurse also touched their hearts and reminded them to have faith: "She drew on the chart in Harriet's room a big circle with a tiny dot in the middle. She said, 'You are the dot, and God is the circle. He is always with you.' We would always draw the circle with the dot when we got off the path. It reminded us very clearly that we were not alone in this."

The true kindness and generosity of the human spirit can be quite stunning and inspirational beyond belief. For instance, Stephen and all of our grown children mentioned how they felt the energy of all the prayers we received. Curious, I asked Carter what it felt like to him. He said, "It's like when I think too much and I am worried this will happen to Stephen again. Then I get a feeling from somewhere that everything will be okay. And I know it is."

During any tragic or challenging time in life, I too have always been distinctly aware that heaven is surrounding me. I believe in the power of prayer and in asking for assistance and guidance on a regular basis. Whether it is God I call on, my grandmother, grandfather, my angels, guides, or simply my higher self, my confidence comes from knowing I am part of something greater and much more powerful than me.

In the moment of that terrifying night when I felt Stephen's life force leaving our house, I came face to face with that "something greater." I felt as if a cloud of energy had surrounded me. Whereas prior to that, the energy in the house felt cold, empty, and stark. The only way I can describe what happened next is that the air seemed to change and became static and receptive. So I took my opportunity at that moment and demanded, and pleaded that Stephen not go. While even though I know his coming back was not up to me, I am beyond grateful that he did.

This experience of communing with "something greater" first happened to me during a profound time in my childhood. I had just been abused — the details of which I will omit here in the spirit of moving ahead in my life—and went outside to sit on the front porch to read the comics and clear my head. I felt alone, scared, sick and confused. Then, I felt a cloud of energy surround me. Light seemed to penetrate my eyes so brightly that I was tearing up. Here I had just been abused but in that moment this energy surrounded me and I only felt love.

Many other caregivers shared similar stories with me about how a window to heaven seemed to open for them too, often when they didn't know which way to turn. For instance, one friend took a temporary unpaid leave to take care of her father, who was alone in another state and dying from prostate cancer. She soon came to discover that her father had serious financial issues and unpaid hospital bills that were mounting.

So after a few months of being by her father's side while paying for his electric and heating bills, her own bills began piling up and going unpaid. About that same time she got a call from work and was told to return to her job immediately or she would lose it. There was no way she could leave her father. Not knowing where to turn, she went to her father's church and joined a prayer group.

Then one week, she was very late for group due to her bedridden father. When she walked in though, she was asked on the spot to share her story with them. She felt like a deer caught in headlights. But in that moment, she also felt her deceased mother's presence nudging her on, to break out of the protective shell that often held her back from asking for help. So my friend went ahead and opened to her vulnerability and told them why she and her father needed their prayers.

Within the next two-month period, home-cooked meals were delivered and groceries left on the front porch. As the weather got warmer, the yard was taken care of and flowers were planted in the large stone pots by the front and back doors. The only items that never showed up were her father's bills in the mail. Not a water bill, or a light bill, and no bills for grocery delivery or lawn care.

Then her father passed. It took another month to get his affairs settled and get the family home in the best condition possible to sell. Five months and one week later, my caregiving friend returned to her closed-up condo in Arizona. She then discovered that her position at work had just become available again. Her employer was so thrilled to have her back that she even got a raise. Her parents' house sold quickly, providing her with enough money to cover her own expenses and overdue bills.

This is a true story.

What does your inspired story look like?

The world would love to hear it.

CHAPTER SIXTEEN

Intimacy, Sex, & The Caregiver

"Sex is like air; it's not important unless you aren't getting any." ~Anonymous

One treasure we can be assured this caregiving journey will bring us is the gift of our evolution as human beings. This "gift of evolution" might, however, temporarily put a damper on our sex lives.

When we become caregivers, we get very used to turning down the patient's bed, tucking the patient in bed, helping the patient out of bed, but when will WE, the caregiver, feel ready to sensually hop back into bed? Along the caregiving journey, a temporary loss in intimacy is almost inevitable. Little or no sex may be the result, as fatigue and stress often rob caregivers of a libido. The other factor too is whether the patient is well enough to frolic.

Restoring desire may take some time, depending on what demands were placed on us during our caregiving journeys. Also due to demands currently being placed on us as a caregiver, desire might very well be the furthest thing from our minds. It makes a great deal of sense then that a revised idea of sensual pleasure might equal a delicious home-cooked meal and a nice warm bath followed by eight solid hours of sleep.

If you are a parent, think back to when you had your first baby. If it wasn't a total blur, you will probably remember feeling exhausted and wondering when, if ever, your sex life would return. Sex was probably an issue (When will the doctor give the ok? When will it not hurt? Will I ever want sex over sleep again?), until it wasn't.

Caregiving can produce very similar results. It's as if almost overnight we become a different person with a new title and increased and sometimes overwhelming responsibilities. Our priorities change and we temporarily stop thinking about ourselves and our own needs and pleasures. Never mind sex. We aren't even in the same zip code of cuddle town yet and don't know when we ever will be. We might even find ourselves questioning if a sense of freedom or sensuality will ever return at all.

It's true that a lack of energy and motivation can limit many activities, including sex. Rest, exercise, and a healthy diet may help to get us feeling better, and even looking better. Let's face it. When we feel good, we feel sexier, but diet and exercise alone aren't enough to get our sex lives back.

Personally, even once I caught up on my sleep and our activities were back to normal, when the cardiologist gave Stephen the big "thumbs up" for sex, I was terrified that my husband would get too excited and suffer another heart attack. (Our dear friend Cynthia Litman even sent me a flannel nightgown to make sure that didn't happen!) Anytime I would think of romancing my husband, I would see in my mind a scene from Nancy Meyers' film Something's Gotta Give (with Jack Nicholson and Diane Keaton). While the age difference between Stephen and me is nowhere near the thirty-year age span depicted in the film, the movie triggered fears for me. Jack Nicholson plays Harry Sanborn, a sixty-something wealthy music mogul who is in the habit of dating women under thirty. While Harry is in the Hamptons romancing Marin Klein (Amanda Peet), things turn disastrous when he has a heart attack during foreplay and is rushed to the hospital.

It took me a long time to get past that image in my mind. I was worried that if Stephen did suffer another heart attack, maybe he wouldn't be so lucky again and survive. How would I ever live with the fact that making love with my husband killed him? How would our adult children handle that little nugget of information? These thoughts and images nagged me.

Sex And The Patient

If the patient has had surgery or has cancer (or some other disease) and is undergoing radiation, chemotherapy or hormone therapy, the treatments or medications he/she is receiving can cause some sexual side effects. Remember, it takes time to heal after surgery, and even longer as we age. So be patient.

Don't be afraid or embarrassed to ask your doctor questions about how treatment might affect sexual function. It's also very important to have a good understanding of what to reasonably expect after treatment is over.

Communication, Communication, Communication!

I urge you to be open and honest with your partner about where you reside on the sexual meter. From #1, "I don't care to ever have a sexual relationship again," to #10, "Drop those bloomers, baby"! Be honest about your own concerns, wants, and needs. And listen. Really listen to those reciprocal feelings of your partner. Together, you and your partner can work together to address what is the best course of action for you as a couple.

If we don't open up lines of communication, not having sex will become the white elephant in the room. But just by sharing with our partners that we are aware of our lack of libido and that we are looking into the issue will comfort him or her and relieve tension in the relationship.

I addressed the issue with Stephen long before I felt ready to resume our sex life. I talked about my fears and concerns, letting him know where I was at and, most importantly, that I was working on "getting over it" while trusting in his patience and understanding.

Try seeking advice from other caregivers, patients, and couples who have gone through what you are going through. Seek professional counseling if you need help understanding your feelings or if you need assistance communicating them to your partner. Online support groups, forums, and discussion groups can also be a great way to ask questions and get the support you need quickly, conveniently, and somewhat anonymously.

You never have to stop making love.

Remember, if sexual intercourse is not happening because the patient's plumbing isn't yet working like it used to due to things such as medications after surgery, there are still many other ways to make love with your partner. Not surprisingly, in talking with more caregivers, I discovered that they often felt like their own sensuality had "left the building" due to stress and fatigue. This further complicated the experience of a healthy sex life with their partner.

Michelle shared:

"When my mother was dying and I was flying back and forth to New York constantly, Mark stayed home to work and take care of the pets. He would anxiously await my weekend return, only to be shoved aside so I could cry, sleep, eat, and take care of all the arrangements.

"I never thought my recovery would take so long. Even when I began addressing the issue of our lack of sex, I wasn't ready. At that point, if I had been lazy about it, I probably could have gone two or three years, quite nicely I might add, without having sex again.

"Sex just seemed like one more thing I had to do and it seemed easier to just let it go. I am so thankful I didn't. If I had let it go any longer, it would have been horrible for my relationship and for my own health, well-being, and self-esteem. I pushed myself to move beyond it, and I am so beyond thrilled I did."

You Have To Feel It To Heal It

As humans, when it comes to sex, we are constantly getting in our own way because we are wired to be the caregivers of our children, extended families, pets, homes, work projects, charities, communities, and more.

As caregivers, before we can begin again to "feel it", we must first begin by being honest (with ourselves and our partners) about why we have been avoiding sex. Is it from a lack of sleep? Is it the fact that we have moved our ailing mother or father into the bedroom next door to ours? Is it because of other increased caregiving responsibilities or the added financial stress? Is it due to our partner recently having had major surgery and we are very worried about their condition? Is it because we have not been able to properly care for our own needs?

As a caregiver, the answer to one or all of those questions could easily be "yes".

We also need to be aware if we are suffering from

depression as a result of our caregiving responsibilities or from life in general. Depression and depression medications are known to lower, if not completely block, desire and the ability to have an orgasm.

We Have Always Held the Key to Unlocking Our Own Libidos

The largest and most powerful sexual organ in the human body is the brain. Sexuality begins right between our ears. We are all well aware that men and women are both wired differently. Yet, while men and women can both be aroused by physical and visual stimuli, the latter tends to be a more powerful stimulant for males.

Women however are more easily stimulated by their imaginations, such as through reading a book or story, or through thinking about a fantasy. For both genders, whatever it is that kick starts your arousal and libido— whether it be with stories, films, images, thoughts, smells, movements, touches, tastes or sounds—understand that it all begins in the brain.

When I was in my late teens and early twenties, I would often fly to visit my grandparents in Oregon. I would then search their home library for books to read. I basically had two choices in styles: Louis L'Amour best-selling novels that my grandpa loved about plain-speaking, straight-shooting heroes of the old West, or Harlequin Romance stories about adventurous heroines who fell in love with the strong, deeply desirable men who they once hated with a passion.

I chose the Harlequin Romance books every time. I was always surprised at how steamy they were and would often sheepishly steal a glance from the corner of my eye toward my grandmother. Once I even asked her if grandpa knew she was reading such things. "Honey," she said with a smile on her face, "he buys them for me."

Oh, my.

Bringing My Sexy Back List

You have likely heard of a Bucket List. I think we all need Bringing My Sexy Back Lists. Whether it is reading a certain book, watching a film that stirs us, replaying an image in our minds that enticed us, learning a new dance, listening to a sexy song, eating a delectable meal, or traveling somewhere exotic, there are many ways to arouse our sensuality. And some of them might even surprise us when they first happen. By all means do not judge yourself. We must not shame ourselves, or others for what works. Just put it on the list!

Many steamy, sexy romance novels become films such as Damage by Josephine Hart, an Irish-born novelist whose bestselling tale of erotic obsession was first published in 1991. The film version of Damage, directed by Louis Malle, stars a seductive Juliette Binoche and a suitably tortured Jeremy Irons who is a member of Parliament. As the story unfolds, he falls passionately in love with his son's fiancée (Binoche) despite the dangers of being found out.

I haven't seen it but Damage is now on my Bringing My Sexy Back List. It may stay. It may not. The fun is in finding what works.

When most men and women read a book, the imagined movie that plays out in their own heads is most often preferred over the version that might show up later at the cinema. Still, some films are equal or even better than the book. Just Google Top Ten Sexy Movies or the Twenty-Five Sexiest Movies Ever Made, and see if you agree! Rent them, download them, or put them in your Netflix queue for that romantic weekend coming up.

 We also can't leave out the opera experience with its sensual scores and lusty, powerful heroes and heroines in gorgeous costume. Think Don Giovanni, Carmen or Salome, during which Salome's dance of the seven veils is one of the most tantalizing opera moments ever.

Sexy Playlists

Many agree there is no better way to get in the mood than listening to some sexy tunes! So let's create our own Sexy soundtracks and add them to our lists for bring our sexy back. Just think: Marvin Gaye "Let's Get It On", or "Sexual Healing", Chris Isaak's "Wicked Game", Dave Mathews Band "Crash Into Me", Edwin Mccain's "I'll Be", Usher's "Love In This Club" or "Nice And Slow", Kings Of Leon's "Sex On Fire", or a little more classic: Frank Sinatra's, "Witchcraft", Serge Gainsbourg and Jane Birkin's "Je T'aime…Moi Non Plus", or the classical Jessye Norman's rendition of "Liebestod".

You'll know what to do if you are a music lover. If not, do a computer search by typing "romantic and sexy playlists" in the search engine along with the type of music you desire.

Food: Sexy, Sensual, Delicious Food!

Ok. This heading needs to be an entire book!

To really get those romantic juices flowing share some sensuous finger foods or a delicious, seductive meal with a glass of champagne or wine with your paramour. Some suggested nibbles are: mangoes, strawberries dipped in chocolate (with champagne of course), oysters, grilled or steamed clams with wine, garlic and tomatoes served with grilled bread for dipping, pomegranates, truffles, gourmet cheese and a rustic baguette, or slowly peeled grapes you feed to your love... one by one! Fun fact: Grapes are associated with Bacchus the Roman God of ecstasy.

Always remember desire can arrive when and in ways we least expect. So when something unexpected pops up in life, just go with it! Seize the moment and go find your partner. The more we begin to honor the moment when we feel sensual, the more often we will continue to feel desirable and want to make love because of all the pleasure, relief, and zest for life it can bring.

"Courage, like fear, is a habit. The more you do it, the more you do it, and this habit—of stepping up,
   of taking action—more than anything else, will move you in a different direction." ~ Tony Robbins

While understanding that returning to your sensual self may take a great deal of courage, I urge you to look at the quote above and consider replacing the word "courage" with "sex" and rereading it.

Learning to care for ourselves as we continue to age is something we need to do, even without adding the title of caregiver or patient. Understand that as time marches on, so will our needs, desires and wants. Loving others, loving ourselves, and our individual sexuality is a huge aspect of self-nurturing and living a healthful life. Dr. Oz even says, "Being in a healthy, fulfilling sexual relationship can do wonders for your overall wellness. Developing science suggests that the benefits range from keeping your heart healthy to helping you look younger."

That alone is reason enough to get frisky!

We must treasure our sexual sweet spots; those very things that arouse us. Whether we find them on the dance floor, in a book, while admiring our partner, when watching a play, an opera, a film, or dining on a scrumptious meal. By doing so we can better assure a return to our sensual selves.

CHAPTER SEVENTEEN

Eating & Exercising For A Better Life

"I would rather eat pasta and drink wine than be a size zero" ~Sophia Loren

Even before Stephen left the hospital, his cardiologist stressed the importance of diet and exercise in my husband's post-heart attack life. To that, I would add "and to the caregiver's life as well."

Make no mistake: proper nutrition and moderate exercise will lift both the patient and the caregiver to new ways of being in the world. However, if change intimidates you, take small steps to see what fits and what doesn't. Change isn't forever unless the strides you have taken honor your well-being and your lifestyle.

Two of the most powerful life changing steps we can take are:

#1. Discovering what combination of exercise honors our body type, age, and lifestyle and then doing those activities on a routine basis.

#2. Educating ourselves about clean, whole foods that honor our individual bodies and lifestyles, and then nourishing our bodies with those foods on a regular basis.

Living a healthful, abundant life by eating a nutritionally sound diet and exercising wisely isn't as challenging, or even as limiting, as we might initially think. For instance, incorporating exercise into our lives can be intimidating, especially if we aren't used to it. So you can begin by keeping it simple. How about lacing up a pair of tennis shoes and going for a pleasurable walk?

Please don't "should" yourself as in "I should jog, I should run, I should race walk!" Instead, try a little less in the beginning and your walk will become a "want to" as well as a source of inspiration and rejuvenation. You can eventually try a little fast walking or jogging on and off during your walk. It will become easier and eventually you might even find yourself enjoying fast walking or jogging for most of your outing.

I love that old commercial where a woman tries all kinds of exercise but nothing seems to fit her. She tries jogging, bike riding, and even walks into a stripper pole workout session, but then promptly leaves. The final scene shows her happily walking, looking radiant. The key is doing what is right for our own body type and lifestyle, and doing something we look forward to and feel happy about.

There is conclusive research showing that even moderate exercise for twenty-minutes a day can produce lasting health benefits, including improvements in your emotional well- being. Even ten or twenty minutes three times a week can make a significant improvement in your overall health.

You might also choose a gym that offers personal trainers, or see a physical therapist who has additional training in exercise therapy. (Insurance might pay for the latter.) It is important to note that as we grow older, we transition into phases where we require more physical activity, not less, in order to keep up with the aging process. For instance, strengthening exercises, stretching and breathing such as in a yoga class, and cardio workouts (as strenuous we can handle, but not more) are crucial components of fitness as we age.

In terms of eating well, there is something "dieters" in particular need to be cautious about. Many people trying to lose weight actually end up hurting their health by severely limiting or even eliminating healthy fats and calories. This can be extremely dangerous. Likewise, many over-exercisers put themselves in the same risk category by placing too much stress on their heart and other organs.

Eating more chemicals while eating fewer natural ingredients in order to save a few calories doesn't lead to good overall health. For example, check out the labels on any non-fat food containers such as non-fat sour cream. Now THAT'S scary! So just because we may be thinner on the outside doesn't mean we haven't aged our insides and stressed our organs from the chemicals we have ingested in the quest to be skinny.

The choice is up to each of us as individuals.

Well, kind of.

We are heavily hypnotized by marketing and words on packaging that make us believe we are choosing something that is healthy for our bodies when it really isn't that simple. Even labels have wiggle room to fudge amounts and calories when listing ingredients.

In the Health Day Reporter article With Faulty Food Labeling, Who's Minding The Store? by Amanda Gardner, the author addresses incorrect nutrition labels:

"Reports in recent months of inaccurate,

misleading ingredient lists or calorie-counts on store-bought foods are leading many to wonder if food-product labeling can be trusted, and who —if anyone —is checking that it's true.

"Consider the following:

"A report published involving twenty-nine reduced-calorie restaurant and packaged foods found that many products had an average eighteen percent more calories than was stated on labels or menus."

The article further says the FDA allows up to a twenty percent variance on nutritive counts. Though the FDA is currently trying to make labels more accurate, I am still wondering, what ever happened to portion control? (I include myself here as well. My family will warn you not to get in between me and a sizzling plate of fajitas!)

My grandfather grew up on a farm in North Dakota and often told me stories of watching his mother make their own butter, cream, whipped cream, and cream puffs. These were simple recipes with a few natural ingredients and obviously no additives. My grandfather's family members were all tall, thin, healthy, and extremely fit. Back then, daily exercise gained through doing chores on the farm was a way of life, as was portion control.

We should ask ourselves: if we eat what we consider to be a "good" nonfat product, do we reward ourselves with larger portions? The psychology of choosing nonfat and lower fat choices then seems to be trading for a tipping of the scales and not a lightening of them.

Embracing a healthy, or even slimmer, lifestyle doesn't have to be severely limiting and might be much easier than we think. Just ask my husband who lost thirty-five pounds in six months, looks fabulous, and says he feels amazing. He eventually discovered for himself that changing his diet wasn't as challenging or as restrictive as he had feared. In fact, he never goes hungry. He just eats delicious food that honors his body and lifestyle so that in a very short amount of time, his quality of life has changed dramatically. Some of this is due to Stephen continuing to exercise. He has always done a lot of cardio but since his heart attack, with my not so gentle nudging, he is now training with weights as well.

We all can probably agree that we often resist the very thing we need the most by imagining the change to be very punishing instead of honoring. Something like joining a gym or a walking group, or taking a strength training or nutrition class, can end up actually becoming both a rich part of our lives and an avenue to enhance our self-esteem. Anything new and out of the ordinary can cause anxiety in the beginning. But just giving something a try can improve the quality of our lives.

Let's talk chow!

I believe that both food and life should be ongoing celebrations. The recipe is simple: If you want a healthful, celebratory life, pick clean foods full of life forces to prepare, cook, and enjoy, while gathering around a table, or sitting on a blanket on the ground, with loved ones. Clean foods are whole foods rich in nutrients, minerals, and vitamins. They are also local, organic, and as seasonal as possible. And, they are meals made from scratch with love. The truth is the more we eliminate processed food from our diet, the more aware we become of our physical and emotional health, and attuned to our spiritual well-being.

A few years back, I had a conversation with renowned author and therapist Dr. Kathlyn (Katie) Hendricks in her own kitchen about how much we both enjoy cooking for those we love. She mentioned how she likes to focus on the chopping of each ingredient and the way she carefully integrates each component while infusing it with love.

When we bless our food by cooking it with love, it is said to enhance the nutritional and spiritual energy of the meal. Try holding your hands over your food as you express your gratitude and notice if you can feel the energy emitting from your hands. You can bless anything, even a glass of water.

Mealtime has brought great comfort to my family and myself during challenging times in our lives. A wonderfully prepared feast is a symbol of great joy and has served as the "fireworks" during many celebrated gatherings. I have found that there are no nutritional supplements that will replace the love and good intentions infused into an organic, fresh, seasonal, home-cooked meal.

Sitting down to a home-cooked meal every evening for dinner was a daily ritual for the children and I as I navigated life as a single parent. It was the one thing I would not take away from my children or myself. One dear friend, during an extremely horrendous time for us, arranged to come by on a false pretense while we were out of the house. We arrived later that evening to a beautifully set table and a card that read, "Dinner is in the oven, dessert in the refrigerator, and you are in God's hands." I still tear up now every time I recall that memory. It was one of the most comforting, loving, and welcome experiences of my lifetime.

This feeling would return after Stephen's heart attack, when friends showed up every night, for well over a week, with home-cooked meals that somehow they managed to prepare on short notice in their own extremely busy lives. Cooking, eating, and sharing at the end of the day continues to be a great source of comfort and stability for us and that tradition continues to this day with our extended family.

If things have turned bumpy for me during the day, week, or month, you can pretty much bet on the fact that I will chop, dice, and sauté some delicious ingredients in order to set the world right side up again. I believe in eating really well. By eating well I mean using food not only to enhance health and well-being but also to fully satisfy the senses and restore the soul.

I am not talking about using food to cope with emotional issues such as loneliness, abandonment, or feelings of inadequacy. I am talking about getting inspired by a recipe or a meal you have eaten at a restaurant and creating meals by going to the market, choosing the freshest ingredients and adjusting the recipe to make it your own. I am talking about eating whole, healthful foods for pleasure while assisting in the reduction of disease as well as in fortifying the body's natural ability to heal itself.

After Stephen's heart attack, he was ready to eat in a way that honored his body and lifestyle. Almost everything from that point on was local, seasonal, fresh and cooked from scratch. He mentioned that his new eating habits felt "replenishing" not "limiting".

I know many of you are thinking, "I work full time. Who has the time to always cook locally and from scratch?" I understand, and am still figuring some things out. But we are definitely finding a much more comfortable rhythm. And the menu doesn't always have to be so strict. The key is trial and error and finding what works for you and your family, while knowing it will get easier. Once you navigate your path and discover what is right for you and your family, you will wonder how you ever ate any other way.

Don't be alarmed though if you find it difficult at first. It can even feel overwhelming to not have the easy way out of reaching for previously prepared or processed foods. But please know the challenge is only temporary. After a while, change becomes habit. These are choices that would be helpful for us all to be aware of and evaluate for ourselves. We need to discover what is right for each of us individually. For Stephen and I, we have learned some great new health and cooking tips that help us to both shed pounds and increase energy.

Ten Tips To Make Conscious Cooking A Snap

1.Plan ahead and shop local. Spend a few hours looking at recipes for the week ahead. Make a list and shop for the freshest ingredients you can find, then adjust recipes accordingly. Go to your weekly farmer's market to get inspired and/or join a local organic produce delivery service that will bring the freshest from area farmers right to your door!

This can often save you time and money.

2. Pre-soak, pre-cook, and store. To make cooking from scratch easier, we can pick a night of the week, or part of the weekend, to soak and cook lentils, beans for chili, soups, stews, salads, and side dishes. Even supposedly "low sodium" canned lentils and beans have way too much salt for heart healthy menus and should be used sparingly.

3. Have rice and grains ready to roll. Make whole grains such as quinoa or brown rice ahead of time and store to mix quickly into recipes. Make a big batch of heart-healthy granola for quick snacks and breakfast. This will save you time and money.

4. Double up. Anytime we are grilling, roasting, or making sauces and soup, we can double, triple, or quadruple the amount we cook so we will have plenty of healthy leftovers and fresh ingredients for lunch, snacks, and last minute dinners.

5. Substitute spices and herbs for sodium. There are many sodium-free herb mixtures and fresh or dried spices full of flavor to experiment with. The less sodium you have in your diet, the more your taste buds will come alive and bring to life many subtle flavors you might be missing out on.

6. Add some kick to your cooking. Look for exotic tasting ingredients to satisfy your taste buds so you will eat less. Also, add some spice to trick your taste buds so you and your loved ones won't crave more fat in order to be satisfied. This really works!

It also speeds up your metabolism.

7. Make special requests. When dining out or ordering take-out, know that most restaurants honor requests to omit cooking with butter, salt or unhealthy additives like MSG. Also, make requests for more organic fresh, local foods at your grocery store.

8. Read labels. Stephen and I are now label-reading maniacs. You will probably be as shocked as we were to read what we were eating on a regular basis.

9. Make your own stock. Making a large batch of stock (chicken, turkey, or vegetable) is a snap. Keep a container ready to go in the refrigerator and then freeze the rest in containers and ice cube trays for smaller amounts. This is a big money and sodium saver.

10. Up the ante on Meatless Mondays by eating plant- based meals more often. Incorporating more plant-based meals into our diet helps our bodies, our planet, and our furry little friends. Eating more vegetarian meals will help us save

time and money, too.

Conscious Clean Eating = Heart Health

Most of us know that heart healthy eating basically means low fat, low sodium, and low cholesterol. It also means including in our diets heart healthy fats like olive oil, coconut oil, canola oil, whole avocado, salmon, tuna, mackerel, and nuts like almonds, walnuts and macadamia nuts. Chia seeds and flaxseed (ground or oil) are also heart healthy additions and easily added to salads and smoothies.

Eating heart healthy also means eating clean, local, and seasonal with higher fiber and a more plant-based diet. This includes much smaller portions of organic proteins (chicken, turkey) and more veggies on the plate. Stephen and I are also eating more wild fish. Unfortunately for my usual preference, it means much less dairy as well. When we have dairy, we focus on low fat as opposed to no fat for more natural ingredients and we consume minute amounts of cheese.

Stephen's major downfall prior to his heart attack was the amount of processed foods he ate such as cereal, bagels, bread, and crackers because they are all loaded with refined flour and sodium. He now stays away from most processed food and doesn't snack after dinner. This pattern is comfortable for him now since he continually eats healthful foods throughout the day and doesn't find himself hungry in the evenings.

One healthy way of reducing your carb craving is by starting your day with a steaming bowl of oatmeal, or home-made heart healthy granola, which is full of omega-3 fatty acids, folate, and potassium. Top your bowl of oatmeal or granola and yogurt with a banana or berries for more fiber.

Most often, Stephen's go-to breakfast is fresh, seasonal fruit, yogurt, and perhaps almond butter on no-sodium bread or apples. He also loves steel cut oatmeal (in the winter and fall) or an egg white frittata that I make with red onion, garlic, broccoli, and a little feta cheese. Throughout the day we snack on fruits, veggies, nut butters, nuts, hummus low sodium rice crackers with tofu dip, smoothies, air popped popcorn, roasted or grilled veggies in brown pasta, lentil, or quinoa salads, and yummy leftovers.

Warning: I discovered that the all-natural, slow-roasted, free-range turkey that I was buying for my son at the deli counter contains way too much sodium. So do most pre-cooked chickens and turkeys, as well as even a simple, frozen turkey breast. Yikes! That is why I suggest cooking extra portions when making those kinds of dishes for dinner so that you have leftovers on hand for lunch or snacks.

Note: Whole Foods and other health-conscious grocery stores usually make a few slow-roasted chickens without any sodium and you can even reserve them ahead of time. Or, try putting in a request for any items you would like at your local grocery store. Most usually respond very favorably as a way to keep you shopping with them.

A little more about Sodium

When we learned about the dangers of high
sodium after Stephen's heart attack I thought I
would be in recovery, regularly attending Salt
Eaters Anonymous. But I managed and my taste
buds adapted rapidly. I remember being shocked
when I pulled out a container of soup that I made
prior to Stephen's heart attack, and discovered
just how salty it was! Yuck. Besides my own
meals made prior to our cleaner eating, it was
astonishing to me to see how much sodium there
is in most foods. Particularly if they are prepared,
canned, or frozen. It is also abundant in bread,
bagels, cakes, cookies and crackers.

Just recently I noticed Stephen's natural, un-
swollen ankles for the first time, in all their
precious little glory! I was so excited. He had
always had what I would refer to as Flintstone feet
and ankles. Now, in hindsight, we know that for
years his body was clearly screaming "No more
sodium!"

Along with salt being hidden in many foods, so too are wheat, gluten and sugar. It is important to make a habit of reading labels to uncover these hidden ingredients and others that can make you unhealthy. I think you will discover, like we did, that by eliminating or cutting down on some of these ingredients, you will feel much better and have much more energy to live the life you desire.

For some of our family's most requested dishes please go to www.DontStrangleThePatient.com and give some of my personal recipes a try.

CHAPTER EIGHTEEN

Wheat, Dairy & Sugar, Oh My!

Or Why?

"The greatest wealth is health." ~Virgil

Just as in The Wizard of Oz when Dorothy and her friends wanted to avoid the dangers of lions, tigers, and bears, (oh my!), we should check in with ourselves and see if any dietary-disease driven problems that we have could be associated with wheat, dairy, and sugar, or any other ingredient we ingest that isn't harmonious with our bodies.

In the New York Times Bestselling Book Wheat Belly, by cardiologist Dr. William Davis, the author describes how wheat and gluten filled products, as well as sugar in all its forms, are major contributors to obesity, diabetes, heart disease, inflammation, cancer, dementia, depression and so many other modern ailments.

Rolling you eyes? I have your back. Skip over the next few paragraphs to the heading Something To Talk About.

Let's Talk Wheat

Dr. Davis says that 80% of the people he meets are diabetic or pre-diabetic. So in an effort to reduce blood sugar, he asks his patients to completely remove wheat from their diets. He says that such a simple change yields incredible and unexpected health benefits in so many more ways than does a drop in blood pressure: "It's about all the other destructive health effects of wheat consumption, from arthritis to acid reflux to schizophrenia, caused or made worse by this food we are advised to eat more of. It's about being set free from the peculiar appetite-stimulating effects of the opiate-like compounds unique to wheat. It's also about losing weight–10, 20, or 30 pounds is often just the start–all from this thing I call wheat belly." ~wheatbellyblog.com

But how can wheat be the bad guy when the bible tells us to eat our daily bread? In part because biblical wheat from our ancestors is far from the wheat we ingest now. For instance, today we consume dwarf wheat, the product of genetic manipulation with much more starch, gluten, and many crazy, coded chromosomes. The wheat we ingest today is also an addictive appetite stimulant.

Let's Talk Gluten

Once, when I was describing a recipe that was gluten free, a friend asked: "Is it wheat-free too?" This gave me pause. Gluten and wheat are terms used almost interchangeably but there is a difference. Wheat is a grain while gluten is a sticky protein and is used to bind the dough in bread and baked goods. It's true that wheat and gluten are always related – but gluten can also be found in other grains such as barley, rye, malt, and to some extent oats. You can have a sensitivity or allergy to one or both too, which means you could consume barley, rye, malt, polenta, and oats if you just have a wheat allergy or sensitivity. If you have a gluten allergy though, you are best off avoiding all wheat, barley, rye, malt, oats, and polenta (unless the latter two are specified to be gluten free).

Dairy

Got milk?

I do and I love it! I also crave cheese, cottage cheese, yogurt, and ice cream. But it doesn't love me back. I will probably never completely give up dairy, even though when I avoid it I feel much better. For example, my congestion clears up and I become headache and inflammation free.

We are hard wired in our country to believe milk is a super healthy, bone building, sports enhancing beverage. Hey, I get it! Nothing tastes better to me than an ice-cold glass of milk with a cookie right out of the oven! I actually "feel'" healthy while downing a yummy glass. However, many scientists agree our bodies weren't made to digest milk on a regular basis. Instead, most agree that it's better for us to get calcium, from other food sources, like whole plant foods such as vegetables, fruits, beans, whole grains, nuts, seeds, and even seaweed.

Read published articles on the dangers of dairy and see where you come in on the dairy meter. Many articles specifically point out that dairy can contribute to heart disease, diabetes, and even cancer. I personally love milk. I also mentioned that I love cheese. One minute we read that natural foods are best and removing fat can cause health issues. The next, we are told the opposite. Who can keep up! As with all changing guidelines and advice, keep an open mind, trust your own intuition, and listen to your body.

I personally am trying to not eat any thing on a regular basis that is cuter or smarter than I am. Lamb out—too adorable for words. Pigs out—both lovable and intelligent. Octopus out. Octopi are considered the most intelligent of all invertebrates and are sentient creatures. One savvy cephalopod was actually caught on camera escaping an aquarium, sneaking out a trap door, and heading toward the ocean. Go man, go!

On the other hand, if you do crave grilled lamb chops, pancetta on everything, or fried calamari, or anything else for that matter, enjoy it with gusto! Life is short and sometimes there are situations when suspension of the limitations we put on ourselves is appropriate.

Something To Talk About

In The Blue Zones Solution: Eating and Living Like the World's Healthiest People, author Dan Buettner provides a refreshing take on longevity and how to get there. He reveals how to transform your health by using smart eating and lifestyle habits gleaned from the communities he's identified as "Blue Zones"—those places with the world's longest-lived, and thus healthiest, people, including locations such as Sardinia, Italy; Costa Rica's Nicoya Peninsula; Okinawa, Japan; and Ikaria, Greece.

Most "Blue Zone" meals depend on simple methods of cooking that have evolved over centuries. The most popular mode of transport is walking and the favorite past time might just be sipping red wine. And more great news—coffee is apparently one of the biggest sources of antioxidants in the American diet. These longevity-friendly men and women tend to eat meat and fish only sparingly, and they almost never tangle with cow's milk. (Pout.)

However, in the New York Times article My Dinner With Longevity Expert Dan Buettner (No Kale Required), by Jeff Gordiner, Mr. Buettner defied the carb-avoiders and gluten-dodgers of America by dashing over to Union Square on foot to score several loaves of long-fermented, freshly baked sourdough. "A true sourdough bread will actually lower the glycemic load of a meal," he said. "But it has to be a real sourdough bread." (Back to good news.)

Now Let's Talk Sugar

What is all the fuss? Can you believe refined sugar has been recently called a toxic drug and is now being targeted as a primary contributor to many chronic illnesses? I recently watch a news program that pointed out that refined sugar is not a food at all it's a chemical.

In an article on The Hidden Dangers Of Sugar Addiction, writer Cynthia Perkins explains how sugar is an addictive drug; "Yes, that's right, an addictive drug and when you remove it from your diet you can experience withdrawal symptoms as excruciating and serious as alcohol withdrawal, including tremors, flu like symptoms, headaches, and mood swings so intense you would damn near kill for a chocolate bar. Some say it is as addictive as heroin.

"The biochemical make up of white sugar is almost identical to alcohol, except for one olecule. Refined white sugar is stripped of any nutritional value and is an empty calorie food; In addition to that, in order to be metabolized in the body it has to draw from your vitamin and mineral reserves and therefore is responsible for depleting mineral and vitamin levels, which in itself creates numerous health problems."

If this is a concern of yours, simply read labels. Refined sugar will also appear under other names such as brown sugar, corn sweetener, corn syrup, high-fructose corn syrup, malt sugar, powdered sugar, dextrose, fructose, lactose, cane sugar, molasses, and others.

Is all sugar equal? What about sugar from natural sources such as honey, molasses, stevia, or agave nectar? Isn't it all the same? Well, yes and no, depending on who you ask. Some sugars and sweeteners are processed slightly differently in the body, with most concerns being raised about refined sugar such as high fructose corn syrup that is readily found in sodas, fruit juice drinks, cookies, cereals, waffles, pies, dairy desserts, and most processed foods.

There was some hope for agave nectar when it first burst onto the health food scene. Many people were excited that it could be a healthy substitute for refined sugar. However, a growing body of research indicates that agave nectar — which is not, in fact, a nectar and is processed in much the same way as high-fructose corn syrup — might be just as unhealthy. (Seriously? I need a cocktail ASAP with a sugar-rimmed glass.)

Now we are told to be aware of one of the most delicious ingredients in the world, pasta. We are notified to be aware of the hidden sugars in carbohydrates like white bread, pasta, and chips and the dangers they can present such as inflammation, high blood sugar levels, obesity, heart disease, diabetes, cancer, failing memory, sexual dysfunction and more.

Anyway we look at it, we are being told that an over abundance of sugar intake can wreak chaos. The book, Sugar Shock, by Connie Bennett C.H.H.C., with Stephen T. Sinatra, M.D., defines this havoc on the body as, "A mood-altering, emotionally devastating, mentally damaging, physically destructive constellation of symptoms affecting million of people worldwide..."

198

Do I think having the occasional frozen yogurt, piece of candy, or eating a few squares of dark chocolate for dessert is going to harm us? No. Actually, high quality dark chocolate can even help us. What I suggest you keep in mind is it's not sugar or the artificial sweetener that's the poison, but rather it's the dosage that makes it poison. So when it comes to sugar, wheat, gluten, dairy, alcohol, or any other indulgence, moderation is key. I am told.

My friend Leslye Dellar described how she cures her daily sweet craving, "I relish and delight in a small morsel of whatever I want with everything I am." She also walks long distances, eats local and organic when she can, works hard, rests often, and is stunning and looks decades younger than her sixty-three years.

3 Simple Go-To Sweets

French Bark Chocolate

I often enjoy a glass of wine for my dessert because it limits my sweet tooth and makes me feel like I am doing something good for my heart. Add a few squares of dark chocolate and you have an incredibly satisfying, heart healthy dessert.

Stephen's cardiologist even mentioned that regularly eating quality dark chocolate could cut the risk of heart disease and stroke. Natural compounds in cocoa and dark chocolate may aid the cardiovascular system by improving blood flow and reducing blood pressure. He also mentioned that scientists have discovered cocoa may help maintain healthy arteries.

At first, Stephen complained that he didn't care for chocolate. He now craves a fabulous French Bark made with the best dark chocolate you can buy, cashews, dried apricots, and bittersweet cherries.

The following recipe comes from my friend Wendy Kuba who would hand out these tasty treats to her exercise buddies in beautiful little packages tied up in bows. It is also how Stephen learned to love chocolate. Pretty easy to do when you start with the best quality ingredients and mix them all together with love.

Ingredients

> 8 ounces very good semisweet chocolate, finely chopped
>
> 8 ounces very good bittersweet chocolate, finely chopped
>
> 1 cup whole roasted, salted cashews (I brush off some of the salt but you can use unsalted roasted cashews)
>
> 1/2 cup chopped dried apricots or other dried fruit
>
> 1/2 cup dried bittersweet cherries or cranberries (yum!)

Directions

Melt the 2 chocolates in a heatproof bowl set over a pan of simmering water.

Meanwhile, line a sheet pan with parchment paper. Using a ruler and a pencil, draw a 9 by 10-inch rectangle on the paper. Turn the paper facedown on the baking sheet.

Pour the melted chocolate over the paper and spread to form a rectangle, using the outline. Sprinkle the cashews, apricots and cherries or cranberries over the chocolate. Set aside for 2 hours until firm. Cut or break the bark in 1 by 3-inch pieces and serve at room temperature.

Note: Scharfenberger or Bernard C. brand can be found at most specialty stores.

Greek Yogurt With Toasted Almonds and Flaked Coconut

Yogurt, combined with some delicious, toasted, organic flaked, coconut and toasted almonds, has become a dessert favorite of ours. The health benefits of combining these three ingredients are off the charts.

Ingredients:

Greek Yogurt refrigerated or soft-frozen

(Check the ingredients of your soft-frozen yogurt. Some are much healthier than others)

Toasted organic whole almonds

Toasted organic flaked (large flakes) coconut

Fresh berries optional

Directions:

Roasting intensifies the flavor of nuts and coconut. Arrange nuts in a single layer on a heavy baking sheet, and bake at 350° for as little as two minutes for flaked coconut, and for five or more minutes for whole almonds. Shake the pan or stir frequently so the nuts and coconut toast evenly as they tend to brown on the bottom more quickly. They're done when they've darkened slightly and smell fragrant and toasty.

Fill a bowl with fresh greek or frozen yogurt and

top with toasted coconut and almonds. Try adding fresh seasonal berries or even a small sprinkle of miniature dark chocolate chips.

Stephen and I are rediscovering that eating healthily and eating for pleasure do not have to be mutually exclusive and it is my wish that you will, too.

Tipsy Pineapple

After Stephen's heart attack, his cardiologist encouraged Stephen to have two glasses of red wine per day. But red wine is not his preference unless it is a very good, expensive bottle....which is fine for a special occasion, not for an everyday event.

Dr. Gomez responded, "I don't care which wine you drink, just get one or two glasses in you most nights. If you're going to drink white wine instead of red, drink some grape juice during the day."

Since Stephen isn't always up to drinking a glass of wine, I found this fun, simple, delicious rum and pineapple recipe in Wicca In The Kitchen, by Scott Cunningham. I like to have it on hand for a late afternoon snack or after dinner treat in the summer. When the pineapple is placed on the grill, it caramelizes and takes on an entirely new flavor.

Ingredients:

1 Fresh, whole pineapple

Light rum

Directions:

Select a pineapple that can stand up. Cut off the top and reserve. Using a long, sharp, flexible knife, cut down and around the fruit from inside the shell about ¼ inch from the sides. If everything goes right, you should be able to lift out the entire inside of the pineapple, leaving the shell intact (You might have to tug a little bit).

Cut pineapple into spears (removing the woody

core) and place in glass container. Pour enough rum to cover fruit. Place in the refrigerator over night. Refrigerate shell and top for serving. When ready to serve, place pineapple spears back into shell and top with crown. Serve with tongs.

Eating pineapple while visualizing your dreams is said to bring protection, luck and money.

For more delectable desserts with a healthier twist please check out
www.DontStrangleThePatient.com.

CHAPTER NINETEEN

Be Alive To Possibility!

The Best Days Of Your Life Are Still Ahead Of You

"The future belongs to those who believe in the beauty of their dreams." ~Eleanor Roosevelt

Up until now, a collective consciousness has permeated our society with the not so subtle notion that once we hit 70, 60, 50, or even 40, the best years of our lives are behind us. The notion whispered in our ears and embedded in our subconscious is: If you haven't lived your dream yet, it's too late now.

Bull-Honky!

Some dreams, like fine wine and cheese, take longer to refine. Some dreams require more than just ambition and desire. They call for patience, wisdom, and a little something called tenacity and divine timing.

I always knew my life would keep getting better as I got older. It probably helped that I was born an ugly duckling and was even forced to wear a full orthodontic headgear apparatus in my teens, making matters much worse. "It can only get better", I would tell myself as I strapped on my metal mouthpiece and leather cranium straps and went out the door.

And, was I right!

As caregivers, this positive outlook may be challenging to maintain. Sometimes our busy lives can cause us to lose focus so we have to learn to get back on the right course toward the life we desire to live. This is where the Life Manifesto exercise and the mantra at the end of the chapter can be useful. So despite your hurdles to overcome, remember there are many reasons why your best days are still ahead of you.

The Facts, Jack

When we become older:

We become wiser.

We become more empathic.

We become better at reasoning because we have a broader understanding of the human experience.

We are more able to anticipate problems and come up with solutions.

We desire to live in the present and not waste a moment.

We are more wired to "Go For It" because we have had the opportunity to develop self-esteem and confidence.

We have learned the power of not giving up.

We have discovered the joy of being authentic because of our earned self-acceptance.

We have learned to appreciate the simple things in life.

We have learned to trust our intuition and to lean on it more.

We trust the power of prayer.

We have gained a broader understanding of the human experience, therefore, a better design for the future.

Getting Better and Happier As We Get Older Isn't A Dream,

It's A Reality.

In an online blog, "10 Simple Things You Can Do Today That Will Make You Happier, Backed By Science" by Belle Beth Cooper, she writes, "It's interesting to note that as we get older, particularly past middle age, we tend to grow happier naturally. There's still some debate over why this happens, but scientists have got a few ideas:

"Researchers have found that older people shown pictures of faces or situations tend to focus on and remember the happier ones more and the negative ones less.

"Other studies have discovered that as people age, they seek out situations that will lift their moods — for instance, pruning social circles of friends or acquaintances who might bring them down. Still other work finds that older adults learn to let go of loss and disappointment over unachieved goals, and hew their goals toward greater wellbeing."

It may be some comfort to you if you worry about your level of achievement to know that most of us don't reach our dreams and goals until well past middle age. This applies to great artists, innovators, and every day people as well. Here are just a few examples of what people over forty accomplished:

AGE FORTY +

Golfer Jack Nicklaus won the Masters.

Julia Child published her book, Mastering the Art of French Cooking.

AGE FIFTY +

Barbra Streisand won a 10-year film and recording contract estimated at $60 million. Go Barbara!

Best-selling American author Sidney Sheldon BEGAN writing his first novel.

 AGE SIXTY +

J.R.R. Tolkien published the first volume of his fantasy series, Lord of the Rings.

Ronald Wilson Reagan was sworn in as President of the United States.

AGE SEVENTY +

 Benjamin Franklin helped draft the Declaration of Independence.

 Grandma Moses started painting and her exhibitions became so popular that they broke attendance records all over the world.

AGE EIGHTY +

At 84, Clint Eastwood directed American Sniper, one of my favorite films ever. It's a powerful experience, and a brave moment in Eastwood's directorial oeuvre. Go, Clint!

At 85, "Coco" Chanel was the head of a fashion design firm.

Michelangelo created the architectural plans for the Church of Santa Maria degli Angeli.

AGE NINETY +

Pablo Picasso was producing drawings and engravings.

George Bernard Shaw wrote the play Farfetched Fables.

ONE HUNDRED + YEARS

Grandma Moses was still painting.

Alice Porlock of Great Britain published her first book, Portrait of My Victorian Youth, when she was 102 years old.

LIFE MISSION STATEMENT MANIFESTO

To help you live your best life we are going to create a life mission statement. Write rapidly and honestly from your deepest desires. Do not censure anything and do not wait for your caregiving duties to end before you start your Life Manifesto. Begin right now or as soon as you have a quiet moment to focus.

Imagine You Are Living Your Dream Life Now

Answer these questions: How are you feeling? What are you doing? What are you cooking? Eating? Smelling? Growing in your garden? What emotions are you feeling? What brings you joy? What projects are you working on? What makes you smile? What are your favorite things to do? When do you lose track of time? Who inspires you? Where do you travel? What do you teach others? What do you share? What would you love to share with others? What matters most to you? What do you strongly believe? What are your finances like? Who is surrounding you? Where are you living? What message would you most like to convey to others and to your world? How can you best use your resources to help others?

Now read over all of your answers and get a feel for your life and who you are in the world. Then pull everything together into your Life Mission Statement Manifesto. It can be more than one sentence — it is a life manifesto after all!

Example: I am healthy, abundant, joyful, full of gratitude for my life — and empowered in all ways living a purposeful life in Oregon with my life mate. I am filled with appreciation sharing time with loved ones, creating, writing, and working to protect our most precious resources: animals, children, and our planet.

Place your mission statement in a prominent place such as on your bathroom mirror and read it once daily. Think about it as you fall asleep at night and when you wake up in the morning. As you read and think about your Manifesto, feel grateful for all of the blessings you have. Know too that your

Manifesto will begin to take on a life of it's own.

Each year without fail, pick a special date, like New Years Eve, to look over and revise your Life Manifesto and to celebrate your progress. If you never give up on your Life Manifesto, and proceed ahead with determination and fully knowing that you will live your best life, you will succeed in doing so!

Life is grand so don't play your role small. Instead, wake every morning with a sense of being alive to possibility so you may reach your fullest potential.

Therefore, allowing us all to experience your masterpiece with you.

CHAPTER TWENTY

What I Learned From This Experience

"People think a soul mate is your perfect fit, and that's what everyone wants. But a true soul mate is a mirror, the person who shows you everything that is holding you back, the person who brings you to your own attention so you can change your life."

~Elizabeth Gilbert

Stephen and I have been given a gift. It became clear to me that once his heartbeat was restored, so was his life...and I later came to find out so was mine. He now has a different sense of himself. For instance, he does not worry. He has no fear and no angst. Not only doesn't he "sweat the small stuff", he doesn't sweat the big stuff either. He is the best part of himself because he is alive to possibility and completely grateful for that blessing.

For me, I feel I have been a witness to a miracle. The ripple effects are changing my DNA as well. I am learning to slow down and to love myself as well as those around me. Through my caregiving journey the voluminous love I have for Stephen exposed itself more brightly. It was a spiritual experience caring for a loved one in their darkest hour. It was an immense honor, one that I will affectionately recall when another caregiving journey comes my way.

Stephen and I have both had an important meeting with the Gods, a face-to-face encounter with Infinite Intelligence, moving us each in our own ways. What I am most conscious of learning is that the present doesn't equal the future, and that every moment is an endowment of possibility.

I am learning to embrace new and live in trust rather than in fear, no matter how uncomfortable "new" feels. I am striving to wake up each day alive with hope and wonder. And equally, I have made a pact to share my life being real, no matter how dark or uncomfortable that may look at times. One thing I know from the depths of my life experience is this: if we can look bravely into our darkness and that which surrounds us, light will always follow.

I now know more than ever that love, and true growth of the human spirit, can have many experiences, terrains, colors, and temperatures.

So embrace your authentic life, dear caregiver. Move toward your dreams.

Live life fully.

APPENDIX A

A Caregiver's Survival Guide To Sanity

~Designate a friend or family member to be the main communicator to all of your other family and friends so you aren't answering dozens or even hundreds of texts, emails, and phone calls.

~Go to www.CaringBridge.org (or many other sites like it— www.lotsahelpinghands.com) and create your own page, or designate a family member or friend to do so, where all communication and information regarding the patient, the caregiver, and the family can be found.

~Accept help. Let me repeat: ACCEPT HELP! If friends offer to cook a few meals, walk your dog, run errands for you, etc., say "Yes, thank you!"

~Copy and distribute the Nurse Ratchet's Helpers Checklist to a few friends and family members. If it makes you feel uncomfortable to do so, just blame me. In other words, let me be the bad guy. Just say, "Nurse Ratchet made me do it!"

~Eat nutritionally well, drink lots of water, and take vitamins if deficient. Limit caffeine, alcohol, and sugar. Pack healthy snacks and meals if you are spending lots of time at the hospital as it can be a little challenging to find nutritious foods in the cafeteria.

~While you are spending time at the hospital or if you are home bound, make sure you get out. Ask any of the nurses and they will tell you that patients need time alone to rest and heal. And frankly, so do you.

~After the patient has been home and rested for

some time, limit guest visitations to a maximum of fifteen minutes each during a designated time of day. Make these rules clear to anyone before they visit.

~Exercise daily: walk around the block, do yoga in the living room, stretch in your bedroom, or simply run up your stairs until you can get back to the gym or on your regular exercise schedule. Moving will do you good physically, emotionally and psychologically.

~Expect hiccups in the routine. Some days will be more challenging than others.

~Learn to say NO. Being a caregiver means it is in your right to use the word "no".

~Give yourself a treat, often. Plan for a date to do something you enjoy.

~Give yourself permission to let some things go, like laundry.

~Breathe and release the tension in your body often.

~Take a quick power nap when the patient is resting.

~Create a new nighttime ritual to ensure a restful night's sleep. Try making and enjoying some warm vanilla milk (see the recipe in the Appendix C, Conscious Cooking Recipes). Draw a lavender or sea salt bath, light a candle and then set an intention. When you are finished, blow out your candle and see your intention infuse into the universe. This is a powerful, nurturing, soothing ritual to offset trauma and exhaustion.

~Take time for yourself daily even if it is just a few minutes alone in the bathroom or sitting outside.

~Express your true feelings. Meet with a counselor or get out and talk to friends. You might be as surprised as I was to see how many others have been in your shoes and completely understand what you are going through.

~Start a journal to express your feelings, frustrations, and gratitude as you move along.

~Plan something fun to do with your partner (or the patient) so the message is clear that this caregiving role does not define your entire life.

~Watch an inspiring movie or read an uplifting book.

~Meet a friend for lunch or a movie outside of the home as soon as you can.

~Visualize the most positive life you can imagine, then blow it up even bigger and see it, taste it, feel it, smell it. Do this at least once daily. It only takes seconds.

~Read your Life Mission Statement Manifesto.

~For a few minutes each day, close your eyes and feel and see yourself on that vacation or life experience you have been dreaming of. Try this hypnotic technique anytime of the day. This will relax, comfort, and inspire you.

~Decide right now that your best years are ahead of you and they will be. Reread Chapter Nineteen The Best Days Of Your life Are Still Ahead Of You when you need clarification.

APPENDIX B

A Caregiver's Guide & Checklist For Helpers

~One friend is to be assigned to be the group communicator so the caregiver and family members are not flooded with drop-ins, calls, emails, or texts.

~Start a CaringBridge.org (or other similar site) website with the family's permission (if one hasn't been created), where communication and information regarding the patient, the caregiver, and the family can be found.

~Identify which family member will be the one to

connect with for arranging meal deliveries and communication. The connecting family member is usually the spouse or partner of the patient but not always.

~If the patient has had a heart attack, heart disease, or any other condition that requires a special diet, send guidelines to meal preparers so they provide healthy, appropriate meals.

~Make a hospital basket for the caregiver (if frequent hospital visits are still occurring) packed with nutritious mini meals, snacks, water and something good to read.

~Visitors need to be positive. Be brief. Be upbeat and then...be gone! Understand that visitations are wonderful but can be draining at early stages, so adhere to the guidelines that have been set.

~If you are available to lend a hand, let the designated friend communicator know what you can do, and also when and how to reach you.

~Don't drink and dial (or text) and share your feelings. The family is almost certainly very sober and your call might seem both intrusive and insincere.

~Don't show up with a bottle of wine (or other libation) the first, second, third, fourth, or fifth night the family is together and expect to stay. They are not in the mood to celebrate and this is not about you.

~Don't immediately share with the family how hard the patient's ordeal has been on you. They have been through enough and don't have the energy to coddle you at this time.

~Know that your prayers make all the difference in the world and that the family, patient, and the caregiver will all feel them.

~Old-fashioned cards or handwritten notes sent in the mail or hand-delivered in a meal or fruit basket are appreciated more than you know because they can be opened and read when the timing is right and remain as a treasured keepsake.

~Leave ONE, and only one, personal message of love for the family with a family member or the friend communicator. I recognize this may be hard, but they will know you are there for them and they will ask for help if they need it.

~Trust that the family members of the patient talk to each other about messages received. Your messages of love and support will be a huge source of comfort and inspiration for them.

~Please don't expect a prompt reply to your note, gift or message. Give them a hearty pass here. Know that time and space equals healing.

APPENDIX C

Holiday Bonus

Caregiving + The Holidays = Heaven or Hell: You Decide

"A perpetual holiday is a good working definition of hell." ~George Bernard Shaw

Warning: Do not host a holiday dinner just a few weeks after your loved one has had a heart attack, stroke, major surgery, or has been diagnosed with a serious disease or illness. Murder or self-combustion may occur! That may seem brutal, rash or flippant, but often after such an ordeal, caregivers aren't in the clearest frame of mind as they remain solely focused on the patient, often ignoring their own well-being.

Most caregivers are nurturers and think about themselves last. We do not realize our limitations until we have far exceeded them. Then it is, "POW! Man down!" (Or Woman, as the case may be.) And that doesn't bode well for anyone in your family, circle, or tribe.

Whining Alert!

I personally knew I was out for the count when I overheard my husband on the telephone tell our daughter how wonderful it would be to have everyone home for Thanksgiving, because we had so much to be grateful for! This was just three weeks following Stephen's heart attack when he had seriously injured himself in cardiac rehab.

This meant daily drives to physical therapy during which the therapist explained how I could properly massage my husband for thirty-minute intervals three or more times daily so he could heal much more quickly.

Knowing I might just be reaching the over-the-top meter, he mouthed the words "you don't have to!"

My husband's joy at simply being alive and wanting to enjoy family and a few nice meals over Thanksgiving wasn't surprising, as he was cuddled up with a blanket on his sofa, with his foot propped up to rest his injured hip, and watching football while having every heart-healthy meal served directly to his side cooked by yours truly.

We did, of course, have much to be grateful for. But when I overheard the call, I had just returned from one of five grocery-shopping trips in the pouring rain and wind in an overcrowded market. Being grateful that my husband was alive didn't stop me from going upstairs to cry alone in my shower, with my cat Sophie fully pressed against the glass, matching my cries with her meows.

In that moment, I daydreamed of receiving some of the care my husband was experiencing.

I wanted someone to serve me meals. I wanted a cute male nurse to fluff my pillows. I wanted sleeping aids and feel-good pills. I wanted to be a happy, grateful patient. I wanted someone to do my chores at home, the laundry, the shopping, and the cooking. I wanted someone else to get up at the crack of dawn and take care of the pets and take out the trash. I wanted booklets on how to take the best care of myself piled up on my bedside table.

Being a caregiver and having patient envy (especially when it comes to your spouse) is a real occurrence. It is okay to be envious of all the care the patient is receiving because we often yearn to be cared for in the same way.

After some reflection and attempts to pull myself together and handle the upcoming holidays and another family gathering in a positive way, I halfway joked to my husband that it was bad manners to have a heart attack around the holidays. (The truth is the Christmas holidays are the time of year when most heart attacks occur. Heart-related deaths increase by five percent during the holiday season. Fatal heart attacks actually peak on Christmas, the day after Christmas, and New Year's Day.)

So caregivers too can easily feel overwhelmed, out of control, and out of patience during the holidays. Holidays alone carry enough pressure to provide a perfect "over the hill and through the woods to grandmother's house we go" experience for loved ones. While others are inundated with fantasy images of perfect families happily enjoying each other's company during a holiday meal, caregivers might actually feel like the grinch yearning for Christmas to just go away.

The six week stretch between Thanksgiving and New Years is the most stressful time of year for caregivers. The added anxiety piled on us around the holidays is due to many things: family members coming home, extra food to prepare, pressure at work, shopping, baking, organizing family outings, transportation, activities, and making sure everyone is comfortable along with all of their other caregiving duties.

It is ultimately up to we caregivers to protect ourselves by creating and enforcing boundaries. Dreaming that loved ones or the patient will recognize our needs and help protect our energy as a caregiver is just that, a dream.

It is not the patient, or any other loved one's fault, that they haven't experienced what we are going through and don't quite understand our current limitations. It isn't their fault that they don't understand during the holidays that even if a meal is brought in, we still have a house full of extra energy, commotion, laundry to do, and other meals to prepare, not to mention our jobs outside the home. We must be gentle with them but firm with our boundaries.

And we must learn to ask for help!!

We can't expect anyone but other caregivers to understand what we are going through. You might even hear some well-intended responses to your hesitation about the holidays: "just don't make it a big deal," or "we will just pick up food," or "I will help you cook!" If our loved ones aren't caregiving on a regular basis or providing the holiday experience for family each year, they won't understand.

Even though you don't have to call off the holidays just because you are caregiving, you do have that option. Remember, a caregiver during the holidays does not don a cape and attain magical "Martha Stewart Home For Christmas" powers. Remind yourself and your loved ones of that.

So, if you are proceeding, you might want to say something like:

"Everyone feel free to come home again for Thanksgiving but please bring your quiet voices, lots of wine, and the food. That will be me on the couch watching movies." Or, "Yes! We would love to come to your house for the holidays this year! Thank-you."

As always too, learn to say NO.

If family were arriving, this would be the perfect time for caregivers to make a fix-it list for them to help you with, such as repair the doorknob that fell off or fix the squeaky window. Also, ask for time off from your caregiving duties and get out of the house.

Be careful as well to not compare the holidays to more simple holidays in the past. Try to be in the present moment with as few expectations on yourself as possible. You can't rush normal. Especially during the holidays.

Being a caregiver during the holidays will also open our hearts and awareness to what others are going through. It can shift our focus to how blessed we truly are. I spent time preparing our Thanksgiving meal thinking about those who have lost loved ones around the holidays. As you can imagine, a painful loss during the holidays changes the way a holiday is framed and experienced forever. My heart was very aware of the many other people in the world who were mourning and I sent out a prayer that they would be surrounded with as much love and support as I have been.

ABOUT THE AUTHOR

Lauren Simon graduated from the Walter Cronkite School of Journalism at Arizona State University and the Mastery Series of Advanced Hypnotherapy and NLP training. Her eclectic life journey has taken her from a successful career as a clothing designer to many years as a flight service operator for a major airline; and from becoming a licensed Reiki master and certified hypnotherapist to film actress. She is also a mother, wife, grandmother, animal lover, fitness activist, and a passionate cook. She lives in Oregon with her husband Stephen, her son Carter, a labrador named Lola and a cat named Sophie.

LAUREN SIMON

The average human heart beats 100,000 times a day. Make every beat count.

PHOTOS & ACKNOWLEDGEMENTS

Our Heroes

L to R: Firefighter Paramedic Daniel Hastie, Engineer Paramedic Shawn Suing, Firefighter Paramedic Michael Doty, and Lieutenant Paramedic Michael Thorne.

Firehouse 59 C Shift

Tualatin Valley Fire And Rescue

Our Family

Cari, Carter, Lauren, Eli, Heather, Stephen, Brianna, Brenna, Olivia, and Tabitha.

From our hearts to yours.

ACKNOWLEDGEMENTS

This book would not exist if it were not for two exquisite men in my life: my adorable husband Stephen and the exquisite Neale Donald Walsch.

If my best friend and charming husband hadn't jolted me into this life and death experience, we would have not grown as much as we have. Thank you, babe. Your support and love are endless and always full throttle.

Neale's encouragement, support, and belief in this book, along with hours of his precious time, ensured that the thoughts and raw feelings that I journaled about would eventually be transformed into this book. Thank you, dear mentor and friend, with so much love, respect, and gratitude.

Much gratitude also to my agent William Gladstone who believed instantly in this book and guided me all the way through the experience...and also to my editor Kenneth Kales whose insights I value and respect immensely.

I would like to express my love and appreciation to my beautiful daughter Brenna whose strength, humor and immense love illuminate my life; my Son Carter who fills me with love and pride for the gentle and kind boy he was and for the responsible man he has become; my adopted daughters, Tabitha the Goddess Of All Things, Cari our lovely, gracious, artistic, Snow White, our still freckle-faced Heather who has grown into a loving wife who teaches us all about the power of positive thinking; our new son-in-law Eli who was sent directly from the heavens; our granddaughters Brianna and Olivia who bring magic and delight into our lives; and to our four-legged angels Lola (our delectable yellow lab) and Sophie (our spunky little rescued cat). Dearest family, your presence brings me joy, peace, and hope. Thank-you for inspiring me to do better daily.

I have been gifted and blessed by wonderful friendships (many have been caregivers) and these men and women have offered valuable insights included in this book. To Sally and Leann who are the most valuable and trusted of dear girlfriends who I can take a deep breath with, drink a few too many glasses of wine with, and let everything out with. To my confidant Jerilyn Hansen, another dear friend, and my "youth advisor," who lights up when we talk about intuition and angels and is the owner of West Linn Aesthetics.

I am also grateful to my father Robert Kirkpatrick and his lovely bride Joyce for their constant support, love, and prayers...to Peggy Keating for being a beloved mother figure and to my Uncle Carter and Aunt Nancy for their positive input and endless support in our lives.

Respectfully, I would like to thank my children's grandparents Ron and Geri Haukedahl for lifting our spirits, providing a sense of safety, and enhancing our lives with what matters the most.

A most gracious, royal curtsey to the very

handsome "Count" James Mapes and his stunning wife, my adored sister in law, "Countess" Susan Granger for contributing to this book and enhancing our lives with a sense of love and adventure.

A loving thank-you to Gay and Kathleen Hendricks for their initial support in jump-starting me out of my journal and into this book.

A huge eternal hug to the eminent cardiologist Dr. Miguel Gomez for saving Stephen's life and for comforting me with his presence when I needed it most and to Dr. Gomez's medical partner Dr. Peter Banitt and his wife, author Susan Pease Banitt, for their enthusiasm and encouragement.

Much gratitude and love to Paul Lewis of Lewis Design and Marketing for his incredible insight, artistry, and support.

A respectful high five to Alexa Weisman for her insightful, funny, and artistic book cover and interior line drawings. You rock, woman!

From my heart, I would like to recognize the Catholic Church for my introduction to the Infinite, for my expectance and knowing that angels will show up, and for respecting the value in ritual. I would like to thank every church pew for upholding me when I needed it, and every minister and pastor for a myriad of stories that assisted in weaving my belief into form.

Within the deepest part of me I thank those unseen who surround me daily, my loved ones daily, and my new caregiving friends daily. May we continue to ask for your help, follow your celestial guidance, and feel your deep love, hope, and the wonder you have for us all.

And thank-you for reading *When You Feel Like Strangling The Patient, Love And Support For The Caregiver.*

Please contact us at...

www.DontStrangleThePatient.com

And...

Lauren on Twitter

@Laurensintents

Lauren on Instagram

@laurencarrolls

When You Feel Like Strangling The Patient

Facebook Page

Facebook/Whenyoufeellikestranglingthepatient

Stephen on Twitter

@Old_Hollywood

25467277R00146

Made in the USA
Middletown, DE
30 October 2015